PLUMBING

A Handbook of Tools, Materials, Methods, and Directions

BY

JOHN G. MILLER

Instructor, Department of Vocational Education,
New York Univ.

D. VAN NOSTRAND COMPANY, INC.

TORONTO   NEW YORK   LONDON

NEW YORK

D. Van Nostrand Company, Inc., 250 Fourth Avenue, New York 3

TORONTO

D. Van Nostrand Company (Canada), Ltd., 228 Bloor Street, Toronto

LONDON

Macmillan & Company, Ltd., St. Martin's Street, London, W.C. 2

PRINTED IN THE UNITED STATES OF AMERICA

CONTENTS

INTRODUCTION

This book deals with the tools and materials that may be used most readily by the home owner, without specific training or experience in plumbing work. Before consulting this book for specific information, the reader is urged to acquaint himself, in a general way, with the contents of each chapter.

Chapter 1 is a fairly comprehensive treatment of the materials commonly used in the plumbing installations in a small house. The various kinds of pipe are described, together with the various fittings, valves, and fixtures that are used with them. Insulation is discussed at considerable length, and methods for installing it are given.

Chapter 2 describes those tools which may be used in plumbing work by the home owner without extensive practice or special skill. Besides those tools used in threading, cutting, and assembling ordinary steel and iron pipe, this chapter also describes tools used for copper or brass pipe, and for making lead joints, in addition to certain tools used for clearing stoppages in drainage work.

Chapter 3 deals in considerable detail with the techniques of pipe work. Specific directions are given for measuring piping runs, for cutting, reaming, and threading pipe, and for assembling pipe and fittings. There are further directions for cutting and assembling copper tube with solder fittings, and for connecting cast-iron pipe. The installation of a hot water heater is described in full detail, in order to clarify the methods previously described.

Chapter 4 gives directions for carrying out eleven representative plumbing jobs that are often required in the ordinary home. In each case detailed practical directions have been given, in order to enable the home owner to undertake these jobs with confidence. Before, however, undertaking any new installation, the reader is urged to consult his local authorities to make sure that it is permissible for him to do this work under the local code, and that his plans have the necessary approval.

Chapter 1

~~~~~~

PIPE, PIPE FITTINGS, VALVES, FIXTURES, AND INSULATION

Kinds of Pipe . . . Pipe Sizes . . . Pipe Fittings . . . Valves . . . Faucets . . . Special Valves . . . Fixtures . . . Insulation: Mixing and Applying Asbestos Cement on a Boiler, Insulating Pipes, Covering Pipes and Fittings . . . Cesspools . . . Septic Tanks

Kinds of Pipe. Probably a hollow bamboo tree was the first pipe to be used for conveying liquids. It is still in use in some parts of the world for conveying water for irrigation. Wooden logs, with a hole bored through the center, were quite commonly used in this country during the last century and, in some places, are still in service. Lead pipe was used by the Greeks and Romans, and vitreous clay pipes by the Egyptians.

The first gun barrels were made of bronze, but to meet the demand for an expensive material, wrought iron was formed into the shape of a tube and then welded by lapping the ends and hammering the heated metal. As the demand for pipe increased, the butt welding process was developed.

Wrought iron was used exclusively for rigid pipe until the last part of the nineteenth century, when Bessemer steel, being cheaper to make, took its place. Today over 95% of ferrous pipe is made of Bessemer and open hearth steel.

Wrought iron and steel pipe are both made in the same manner. A flat piece of metal, called a skelp, is heated in a gas furnace and, when it has reached a temperature of 2450° F., it is drawn through a *welding bell*, which forms the skelp into pipe of the size required and, at the same time, welds the seam, by the intense heat and pressure that are applied to the pipe as it is being drawn through the bell. Modern pipe welding machines attain a high rate of production. For instance, $\frac{1}{2}''$ pipe may be drawn and welded at the rate of 1100 lengths per hour, or the equivalent of 100 miles in 24 hours.*

Almost all steel and wrought-iron pipe is *galvanized* on both the outside and inside in order to resist corrosion. Black iron pipe (not galvanized) is normally cheaper than galvanized. Iron pipe (not galvanized) is suitable

---

* Jones and Laughlin Steel Corp.

for use as piping in heating systems, both steam and hot water. It is also used extensively for gas and oil pipe lines.

Black iron pipe is not suitable for use to convey water in either supply or drainage systems, as it rusts readily and will cause stoppage in a relatively short period of time. Galvanized-iron pipe is a standard item for supply and drainage in the home plumbing system, because of its low cost and its relatively high resistance to corrosion.

Genuine wrought-iron pipe is usually marked by the manufacturer as such, and it may be obtained either black or galvanized. In comparison with common iron pipe, it has a superior resistance to rust formation, and therefore the higher initial cost is often offset by longer service.

Wrought-iron and steel pipe are usually supplied in single random lengths of 21′, in sizes of ⅛″ to 12″ nominal inside diameter, threaded at both ends, with a coupling screwed on one end.

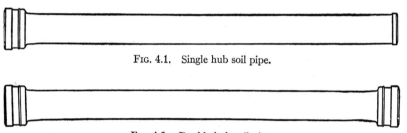

Fig. 4.1.   Single hub soil pipe.

Fig. 4.2.   Double hub soil pipe.

Cast-iron soil pipe has been used for drainage work for years. The most common type of C.I. pipe used in domestic work is known as "C.I. Bell & Spigot" pipe. Two typical straight lengths are shown in Figs. 4.1 and 4.2, a single hub and spigot piece and a double hub length. The wall thickness of C.I. pipe for any given size is available in any of the following weights: 1 standard, 2 medium, and 3 extra heavy (XH).

The use of the lightest weight (standard) pipe is limited or prohibited by most building codes for all but above-ground work, or in vent stacks above the highest plumbing fixture in the building. Extra heavy soil pipe, always marked *XH* near the hub, is customarily required for all underground drainage lines inside buildings, and all interior drainage lines above ground, including soil, waste, and vent stacks. The most common sizes used are 2″, 3″, 4″, 5″, and 6″, and they are commonly supplied in standard lengths of 5′, measured from end of spigot to bell.

Brass pipe has replaced galvanized iron pipe to a great extent in the past few years. Brass pipe offers all the advantages of iron pipe, plus the fact that it does not rust. When installed in a building, a system using brass pipe and fittings will last the life of the building. The longer life reduces the maintenance cost of the plumbing. The smoother interior surface of brass pipe will permit the water to flow with less friction. Therefore, a greater volume of water will flow through brass pipe than through steel pipe of the same size.

NEW INSTALLATION

Larger size pipe required for full flow.

Smooth inside walls provide full flow using smaller pipe.

A FEW YEARS OF SERVICE

Diminished flow — rust-colored water, replacement necessary.

Same full flow of rust-free water — as good as new.

Fig. 4.3. The advantage of brass pipe.

This fact produces a saving in pipe sizes when brass is used instead of iron. When employing brass pipe, use one size smaller than that of the iron pipe which would be required. This saving in pipe and fittings, plus the greater life of service, makes brass pipe more economical than iron pipe. Brass pipe will withstand a pressure of 1000 lbs. per sq. in. It is manufactured in 12' lengths up to 4" diameter.

Copper tubes with flanged fittings have been used in automotive gasoline and oil lines for many years. Although copper water tubing has been used successfully for many years in Europe and other parts of the world, its use in plumbing in the United States is comparatively recent. Copper tubes with flared or flanged fittings, and also with soldered or sweated fittings, are now being used extensively in heater coils, refrigerators, and other mechanical appliances.

The popularity of copper tubing is due partly to its ease of installation. It is soft enough to be bent easily around obstructions. It can be run between

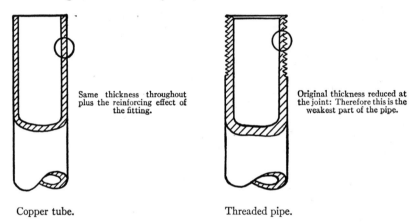

Same thickness throughout plus the reinforcing effect of the fitting.

Original thickness reduced at the joint: Therefore this is the weakest part of the pipe.

Copper tube.   Threaded pipe.

Fɪɢ. 4.4.   Advantage of copper tube at the joint.

studding and floor beams in uninterrupted runs without the use of fittings. Sometimes the removal of a base or floor board is all that is necessary to make a replacement during alterations or repairs. It is rigid enough to be strung up in long lengths without undue sagging, provided tubing of hard temper is used. It is economical in the sense that there is no weakening of the pipe at the joint as in threaded pipe, where the original thickness of the pipe is reduced. Copper tubes with sweated or flanged fittings can therefore be much thinner than threaded pipe, without being weak at the joints.

Copper tubes are corrosion resisting under normal conditions. They stand up under the rough usage that pipes usually get when being installed. Although hard-drawn copper tubes are as readily damaged by freezing water as iron pipe, soft or annealed copper tubes actually resist the bursting caused by freezing water. Tests have shown that $\frac{1}{2}''$ annealed tubes have been frozen as many as six times before they finally burst. Tests also have shown that both iron pipe and hard copper tubes burst during the first freezing. The flexibility and ductility of the soft or annealed copper tubing make it particularly suitable for underground water service, where the hard copper tube would not be practicable. There is always a certain amount of unequal settlement of the ground, especially where pipes are buried. Therefore, in choosing and installing underground pipes, provision must be made for this movement. Care must be taken to give additional protection to soft tubing by burying it well below frost level, which varies according to geographical location.

Copper tubes may be expected to last as long as the building in which they are installed, provided they are used under normal conditions and ordinary care and skill is used in their installation.

Copper tubing may be classified as to its wall thickness and also its hardness. Wall thicknesses are either light (type L), or heavy (type K). Types K and L are available in either the hard (cold drawn) or soft (annealed) tubes. Unless there is reason to believe that the water being used is unusually corrosive, type L tube has sufficient wall thickness. For service pipes to the street it is advisable to use heavy wall thickness tubing (type L soft).

STANDARD SPECIFICATIONS FOR TYPES K AND L SEAMLESS COPPER TUBE

Nominal Size, Inches	Outside Diameter, Inches	Inside Diameter, Inches		Wall Thickness, Inches		Permissible Variation of Mean Outside Diameter		*Pounds per Linear Foot	
	Types K-L	Type K	Type L	Type K	Type L	Types K-L		Type K	Type L
						Annealed	Hard Drawn		
⅛	.250	0.186	0.200	.032	.025	.002	.001	0.08495	0.06849
¼	.375	.311	.3 5	.032	.030	.002	.001	.1337	.1260
⅜	.500	.402	.430	.049	.035	.0025	.001	.2691	.1982
½	.625	.527	.545	.049	.040	.0025	.001	.3437	.2849
⅝	.750	.652	.666	.049	.042	.0025	.001	.4183	.3621
¾	.875	.745	.785	.065	.045	.003	.001	.6411	.4548
1	1.125	.995	1.025	.065	.050	.0035	.0015	.8390	.6545
1¼	1.375	1.245	1.265	.065	.055	.004	.0015	1.037	.8840
1½	1.625	1.481	1.505	.072	.060	.0045	.002	1.362	1.143
2	2.125	1.959	1.985	.083	.070	.005	.002	2.064	1.752

* Slight variations from these weights must be expected in practice.

Hard tubing is generally furnished in lengths of 20′, straight and uncoiled. Soft tubes are furnished in 20′ lengths and in coils of 30′, 45′, 60′, and 100′ in sizes up to 1″ diameter. Larger sizes usually come in 20′ lengths.

Lead pipe has been largely replaced by brass pipe and copper tubing. Its advantages are resistance to corrosion and flexibility. It can be easily bent around corners, and into other special shapes. Lead pipe is used for underground service, and for traps and waste connections to some plumbing fixtures, such as water closets.

Vitrified soil pipe is a clay pipe which is used for drainage outside a building. This type of pipe comes with a flanged end which forms its connection with another pipe of the same material, or with cast-iron soil pipe. Several standard fittings for this type of pipe are also on the market for making branches and turns necessary in an outside drainage system. The sizes of these pipes are measured on the inside, and run from 2″ to 6″ in diameter. Pipes are made in 2′, 2½′, and 3′ lengths. A convenient length is the 3′ length, as a run of pipe of this length requires less joints. Vitreous clay pipe is not recommended for drainage inside a building as the joints are brittle, and cracking results from a slight movement. Vitrified pipe will outlast almost any other material providing it does not crack or break. Extra heavy pipes are useful where heavy stresses are anticipated.

Pipe sizes are usually determined by the diameter of the inside of the pipe. An exception to this rule is found in iron and brass pipe which are used with

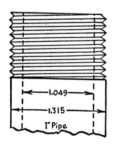

Fig. 4.5. Dimensions of 1″ iron pipe.

threaded fittings. These pipes have an inside diameter slightly larger than the nominal size. Originally, pipe was made with heavier wall thickness due to weakness in materials. As stronger materials were developed, thinner walls were possible. Instead of decreasing the outside diameter and keeping the inside diameter the same, the hole size in the pipe was enlarged, keeping the original outside diameter. This made it possible to continue the use of standard tools and fittings on the thinner-wall pipe. Due to this fact, nominal sizes of threaded iron and brass pipe are slightly smaller than the inside diameter. This is most noticeable with the smaller sizes, particularly ⅛″ pipe. It measures about ¼″ inside diameter and more than ⅜″ outside diameter.

To determine the size of iron or brass pipe, measure the outside diameter of the pipe with an outside caliper and use the table below.

To determine the size of copper or brass tubing, lead pipe, cast iron, soil pipe, or vitreous clay drain pipe, measure the inside diameter of the pipe.

Pipe Fittings. *Screwed pipe fittings* for use on threaded pipe for water supply, drainage, heating, and gas pipe, are available in many forms. They

DETERMINING SIZE OF IRON OR BRASS PIPE

Nominal size of pipe	$\frac{1}{8}''$	$\frac{1}{4}''$	$\frac{3}{8}''$	$\frac{1}{2}''$	$\frac{3}{4}''$	$1''$
Approximate inside dia.	$\frac{1}{4}''$	$\frac{3}{8}''$	$\frac{1}{2}''$	$\frac{5}{8}''$	$\frac{13}{16}''$	$1\frac{1}{16}''$
Approximate outside dia.	$\frac{3}{8}$	$\frac{17}{32}''$	$1\frac{1}{16}''$	$\frac{13}{16}''$	$1''$	$1\frac{5}{16}''$

Nominal size of pipe	$1\frac{1}{4}''$	$1\frac{1}{2}''$	$2''$	$2\frac{1}{2}''$	$3''$	$3\frac{1}{2}''$	$4''$
Approximate inside dia.	$1\frac{3}{8}''$	$1\frac{5}{8}''$	$2\frac{1}{16}''$	$2\frac{9}{16}''$	$3\frac{1}{16}''$	$3\frac{9}{16}''$	$4''$
Approximate outside dia.	$1\frac{5}{8}''$	$1\frac{7}{8}''$	$2\frac{3}{8}''$	$2\frac{7}{8}''$	$3\frac{1}{2}''$	$4''$	$4\frac{1}{2}''$

are used for the purpose of joining, changing direction, branching, reducing, and capping pipe.

Cast-iron fittings for threaded pipe may be used for heating systems and will withstand 125 lbs. per sq. in. pressure with safety. Extra heavy fittings are available for higher pressures.

Malleable iron fittings are more common than cast-iron fittings. They are available in either galvanized or black iron. Black iron fittings are used for heating systems and gas pipe lines. Galvanized iron fittings are used for water supply and drainage fittings, where galvanized iron pipe is installed. Malleable iron fittings will withstand higher pressures than cast iron and, at the same time, are more uniform on the outside and of less bulk. These fittings are available in plain and beaded, or flat band, patterns. The plain pattern is for use in low-pressure house plumbing, while the beaded or flat band is intended for higher pressures.

Brass fittings, used for connecting brass pipe, come in standard and extra heavy weights. They are made in the same styles as the malleable iron fittings.

When choosing the fittings to be used on a job, it is a good idea to use only the simplest fittings. Special fittings are costly, and usually hard to obtain. Some of the most common fittings are listed in the accompanying illustration (Fig. 4.6).

Fittings are ordered of the same size as the pipe on which they are to be used. Reducing fittings are ordered as follows (see Fig. 4.7):

Reducing elbows: Give size A and B.
                          Example: $\frac{3}{4} \times \frac{1}{2}$ "L".

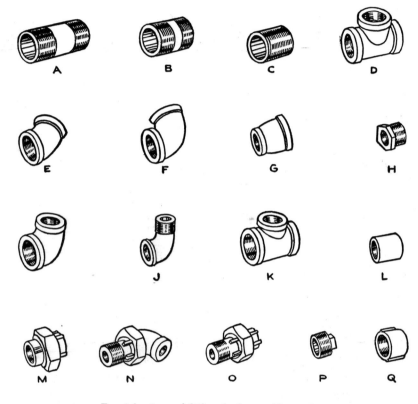

FIG. 4.6. Screwed fittings for iron and brass pipe.

A. Long nipple, usually 3, 4, 5 or 6″ long.
B. Short nipple (length varies with diameter of pipe)
C. Close nipple (length varies with diameter of pipe).
D. Tee or "T" fitting.
E. Forty-five degree elbow or 45° "L".
F. Ninety-degree elbow or "L".
G. Reducing coupling or reducer
H. Bushing (hex head bushing).

I. Reducing elbow.
J. Street elbow.
K. Reducing tee.
L. Coupling.
M. Union
N. Elbow union.
O. Tank union.
P. Pipe plug.
Q. Pipe cap.

Reducing tees: Give size A, then B, and last C.
    Either size of B or C may be reduced or both.
    Example: 1 × ¾ × ¾ "T".

Hex head bushings: Give size A and B.
    Example: 1¼ × ¾ bushing.

Reducing couplings: Give size A and B.
    Example: 1 × ¾ coupling.

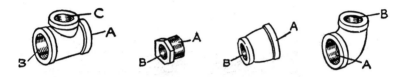

FIG. 4.7.   Designating the size of reducing fittings.

Reducing fittings usually reduce only one size, from a given size to the next size smaller.   However, bushings which reduce two or more sizes are quite common.

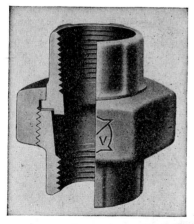

FIG. 4.8.   Common gasket type union.
Courtesy The Kennedy Valve Mfg. Co.

FIG. 4.9.   Union with ground brass seat.
Courtesy E. M. Dart Mfg. Co.

Unions are made in two general types: (a) the old style gasket type, which requires a fiber gasket at the joint of the two members and (b) the brass-seated union, which requires no gasket, as a watertight joint is obtained by the brass inserts at the seat of the fitting. The latter has replaced the former in most plumbing systems, and is used universally in systems made up of brass pipe and fittings.

Shoulder of drain pipe slows flow of water & collects solid waste matter.

No shoulder to catch solid matter.

FIG. 4.10.   FIG. 4.11.

Drainage fittings are especially adapted to take care of drainage work where a screwed fitting is used. These fittings, sometimes called Durham

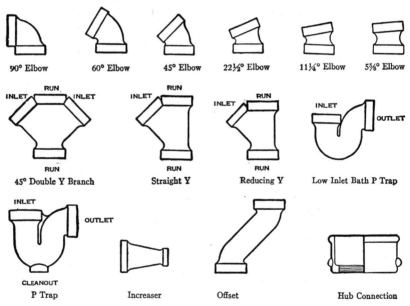

| 90° Elbow | 60° Elbow | 45° Elbow | 22½° Elbow | 11¼° Elbow | 5⅝° Elbow |

45° Double Y Branch   Straight Y   Reducing Y   Low Inlet Bath P Trap

P Trap   Increaser   Offset   Hub Connection

FIG. 4.12.   Cast-iron drainage fittings. Screwed for wrought pipe.

fittings, after the name of their inventor, are constructed with a thread that is recessed, so that there will be no projecting shoulder in the pipe to catch solid matter at the joint.

Figure 4.10 shows how solid matter may cause stoppage when ordinary fittings are used for drainage, while Fig. 4.11 shows how drainage fittings help prevent stoppage at the joint.

These fittings come in a large variety of shapes for the purpose of branching, venting, and joining threaded drainage pipe in the sewage disposal system. These include almost all the fittings that are supplied for cast-iron drainage systems, such as traps and roof connections. The main advantage of this type of disposal system is that the threaded fittings afford a more permanent watertight joint, and the space necessary for fittings is less than for the fittings required in the use of cast-iron soil pipe. When fixtures must be placed in close quarters, it is advisable to use this type of fitting to save space. The cost of this type of an installation is necessarily much higher than that of cast-iron soil pipe.

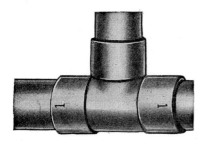 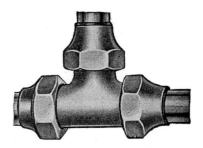

FIG. 4.13. Soldered type fitting for
copper tube.

FIG. 4.14. Flanged type fitting for
copper tube.

Copper tube fittings are available in practically every form in which screwed fittings are supplied. In addition, there are special adapters for joining copper tube to threaded pipe of iron pipe size. Manufacturers' catalogs, which are furnished upon request, contain complete lists of these fittings.

Cast-iron fittings are used for making turns, branch connections, or other sharp changes in direction of a line of C.I. drainage pipe. These fittings have bell and spigot ends, threaded ends, or a combination of the two. Sketches 1–29 inclusive illustrate a complete line of the most common fittings used for drainage pipe work. The sizes of fittings are always stated as the nominal pipe size. When a change in size occurs, as in the case of reducing tees, crosses, increasers, etc., the largest run opening is given first, followed by the opening at the other end of the run. When the fitting is a tee, the outlet size is given next. For a cross, the run openings are given first, followed by the cross openings in order of size.

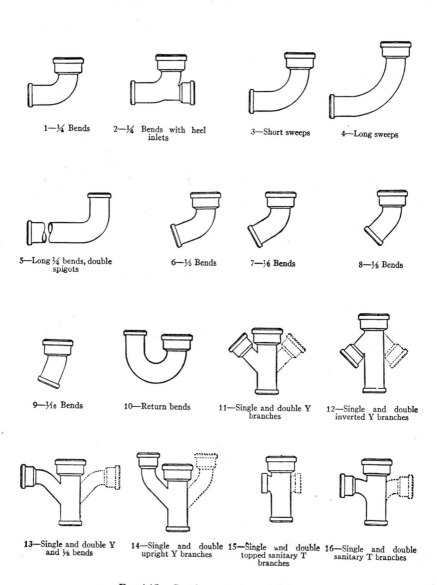

1—¼ Bends   2—¼ Bends with heel inlets   3—Short sweeps   4—Long sweeps

5—Long ¼ bends, double spigots   6—⅕ Bends   7—⅙ Bends   8—⅛ Bends

9—¹⁄₁₆ Bends   10—Return bends   11—Single and double Y branches   12—Single and double inverted Y branches

13—Single and double Y and ⅛ bends   14—Single and double upright Y branches   15—Single and double topped sanitary T branches   16—Single and double sanitary T branches

Fig. 4.15.   Cast-iron soil pipe and fittings.

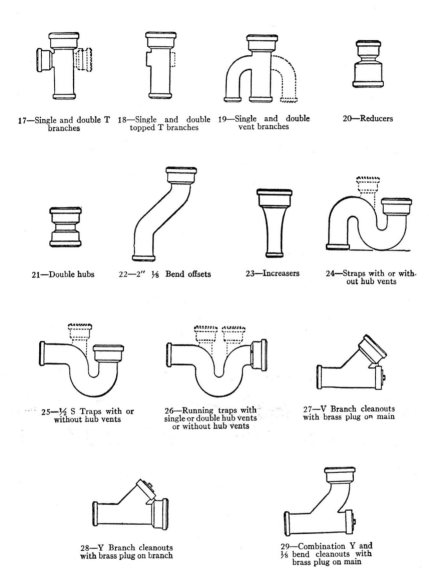

17—Single and double T branches   18—Single and double topped T branches   19—Single and double vent branches   20—Reducers

21—Double hubs   22—2" ⅛ Bend offsets   23—Increasers   24—Straps with or without hub vents

25—½ S Traps with or without hub vents   26—Running traps with single or double hub vents or without hub vents   27—V Branch cleanouts with brass plug on main

28—Y Branch cleanouts with brass plug on branch   29—Combination Y and ⅛ bend cleanouts with brass plug on main

Fig. 4.15. Cast-iron soil pipe and fittings.

Valves. A valve, as the term is used in plumbing, is a device for controlling the flow of liquids or gases through a pipe.

Valves are made of malleable iron (black or galvanized), brass, bronze, or cast iron. Valves and faucets used in household plumbing are usually made of solid brass. They are made either in plain, nickel-plated, or chromium-plated finishes. There has been a tendency recently to make some faucets of white metal alloys, as these stand polishing better than the plated finishes.

All valves fall into one of the two following classifications, automatic or manual. Most of the valves included in the household water supply and drainage system are of the manual type; however, in the heating system there may be several automatic valves, the most common of which is the valve which lets the air out of a radiator in a steam heating system.

Selection of Valve. In selecting the valve to be used, the first consideration is the quantity of fluid which the valve permits to pass. This will vary with the type of valve under the general principle that, the greater the degree of pressure control, the greater the restriction of flow.

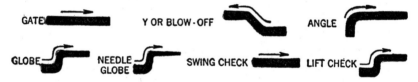

FIG. 4.16. Diagram showing the extent and direction of flow of liquid through common types of valves. *Courtesy of Jenkins Bros.*

Gate valves allow maximum flow, *angle* valves allow medium flow, while *globe* valves slow the flow of water considerably, and *needle* valves offer the closest control; therefore, the least flow. The *key* type of valve, that is used to a great extent in the control of gas in the home, is as efficient as the gate valve and also has the advantage of quick operation, requiring only a one quarter turn to open or close it. *Check* valves are used to prevent reverse flow of a liquid through a pipe line, and are usually placed near the discharge end of a pump, to keep the water in the pipe from flowing back through the pump.

Gate Valves. Valves which control the flow of water by closing a sliding gate, which is usually operated by a spindle screw, are known as gate valves. Gate valves of common household sizes are usually constructed so that the spindle does not rise. The main advantage of a gate valve is that the flow of water is not impaired by the installation, and there is no washer to be

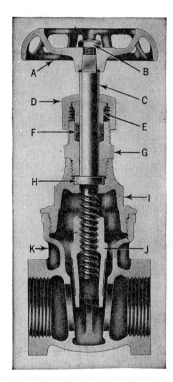

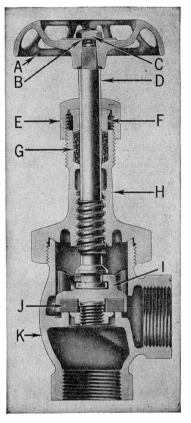

Fig. 4.17.   Section through a gate valve.

A.	Hand wheel.
B.	Wheel nut.
C.	Spindle.
D.	Packing nut.
E.	Gland.
F.	Packing box.
G.	Packing box nipple.
H.	Spindle collar.
I.	Bonnet.
J.	Solid wedge.
K.	Body.

Fig. 4.18.   Angle type of globe valve.
Courtesy of Jenkins Bros.

A.	Hand wheel.
B.	Index plate.
C.	Hand wheel nut.
D.	Spindle.
E.	Packing nut.
F.	Gland.
G.	Packing box.
H.	Bonnet.
I.	Disk holder.
J.	Composition disk or washer.
K.	Body.

replaced when worn. Gate valves are especially recommended for controlling the flow of water in the main supply line, where the flow of water is seldom interrupted, and the quantity of flow is the main consideration.

Globe Valves and Angle Valves. Globe valves are closed by forcing a washer disk down upon the valve seat by means of a screw on the spindle of the valve. An angle valve is a special type of globe valve, essentially the same except for the fact it changes the direction of the pipe 90°. Globe valves are made either with a composition washer or a ground metal disk fitting against ground seats. The latter type of valve is designed for use in hot water or steam lines. An objection to this type of valve is that it cannot be repaired easily if a leak develops, whereas the washer type can be maintained by replacing the washer.

FIG. 4.19.   Solder-end valve for copper tubing.
Courtesy of Jenkins Bros.

A globe valve should be installed so that the direction of water flow is up through the orifice, and so that the washer is moved against the flow when closing. In spite of the decreased flow due to the small size of the orifice, the globe valve is widely used in household plumbing. The angle valve offers less restriction to the flow of water and can be economically used in close places, eliminating one fitting in the pipe line.

Radiator Valves. Either gate or globe valves are available with special construction so they can be used as shut-off valves for radiators. These valves are usually fitted with a male union nipple which screws into the radiator. This nipple is designed with a spherical radius on its face to insure proper seating against the valve when it is in position.

Solder-end Valves. These valves are available in both globe and gate types for use with soldered fittings on copper tubing.

Needle Valves. Valves of this type are used where there is to be a limited flow of liquid or gas, and where a very fine adjustment is essential.

Check Valves. These valves are used to prevent reverse flow of water in a pipe line. There are many types of check valves. They operate on the principle that a reversal of flow in the pipe will cause the hanger to drop, closing the orifice in the valve.

Ground-key Valves. This type of valve is used almost exclusively as the curb "shut-off," and as a means of controlling gas supply. Its main advan-

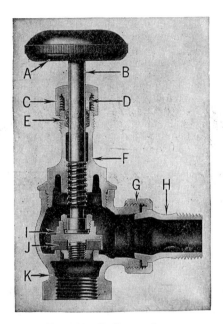

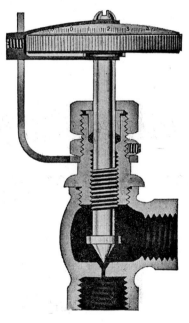

Fig. 4.20.   Radiator valve.
Courtesy of Jenkins Bros.

Fig. 4.21.   Globe type needle valve.

A. Hand wheel.
B. Spindle.
C. Packing nut.
D. Gland.
E. Packing box.
F. Bonnet.

G. Union ring.
H. Union nipple.
I. Disk holder.
J. Composition disk or washer.
K. Body.

tage is that the flow is not impaired, as the orifice in the key is the size of the pipe opening. The shut-off requires only one quarter-turn, so that its action is quick. Valves of this type have no fiber washer to replace; however, a faulty key will make the valve useless, and its replacement necessary.

Radiator Air Valve. As ordinary water used to generate steam in a heating system contains a certain amount of air, and since steam pipes, when not filled with steam, contain air, it is necessary to provide a means of escape for this air if the system is to function properly.　A hand-operated valve placed at the top of a hot water radiator will vent the trapped air and improve circulation of the hot water.　This type of valve, however, is not suitable for steam radiators, because it would need continual attention.

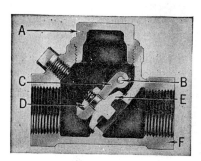

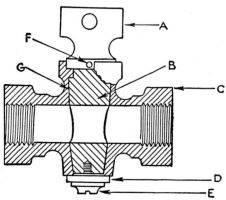

Fɪɢ. 4.22.　Horizontal swing check valve.
Courtesy of Jenkins Bros

A. Cap; B. hanger pin; C. hanger; D. hanger nut;
E. disk; F. body.

Fɪɢ. 4.23.　Ground key valve, open
position.

A.　Key　　　　　　　　　　D.　Washer.
B.　Conical valve.　　　　　E.　Retaining screw.
C.　Hex head.　　　　　　　F.　Stop pin.
　　　　　　　G.　Ground-valve seat.

An automatic valve is the proper type to use on steam radiators.　Automatic valves provide for the escape of the air and close automatically when steam or hot water reaches them.　These valves are placed on the end of the radiator, about one third to one half of the distance from the bottom, because of the fact that air is heavier than steam.　It is to the advantage of the home owner to install the best quality air valves in his heating system, as an efficient valve is a fuel saver.　Some of the air valves on the market stay closed after the air is expelled from the radiator, thus creating a partial vacuum in the heating system.　This is advantageous, because it causes the water in the boiler to change to steam at lower temperatures, permitting more efficient use of the heat.　In order that this type of valve function properly, it must be installed throughout the heating system.　Other possible openings where leakage might occur, such as the packing about the spindle of the shut-off valve on the radiator, must be closed.

Safety Valves.　These valves are installed on steam boilers to prevent the steam pressure from rising above a predetermined safe working pressure. The proper operation of this valve is essential to the safety of the occupants of the house (Fig. 4.25). A lever is usually provided on the valve, by which

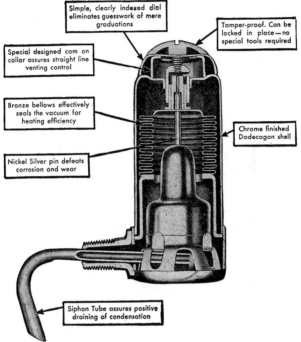

FIG. 4.24. Vacuum type air vent valve. *Courtesy of Dole Valve Co.*

it may be opened periodically to make sure that it is not sticking to the seat. It is a good plan to know the pressure at which the valve will "pop," and to use this as a guide in regulating the fire. Manufacturers usually attach a tag to the valve, showing its operating pressure. *Do not tamper with this valve!*

Flush-ball Valve. This type of valve is used in the closet tank for the purpose of admitting water to the closet in flushing. This valve is usually operated by a trip lever, which causes the ball to rise. The air in the ball keeps it in the open position until the tank is emptied, and the ball valve drops into the valve seat, stopping the flow of water from the tank. An overflow pipe is usually provided as an integral part of the valve-seat, so that the water will not rise above its level due to a leaky inlet valve.

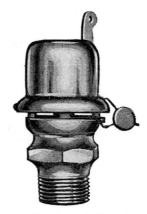

FIG. 4.25.   Steam boiler safety valve.
Courtesy of Bohn Aluminum & Brass Corp.

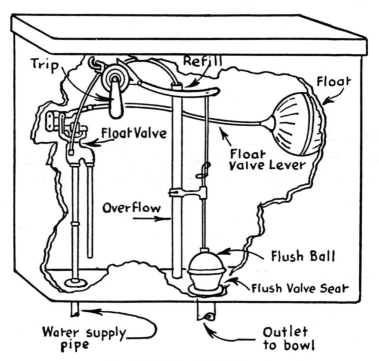

FIG. 4.26.   Mechanism of flush tank.

Float Valve. This valve is used to control the flow of water into the flush tank. The quantity of water in the tank when filled is determined by the height of the *float* when the valve is closed. When the water is emptied from the tank by the action of the trip on the ball valve, the float drops, opening the float valve, and thus letting water into the tank. A refill tube is provided, which allows a small amount of water to go into the bowl through the overflow pipe. This assures the filling of the trap in the bowl to the maximum height. When the float reaches its original position, the valve closes, and the tank is ready for the next flush.

Automatic Flush Valve. Flush valves which will take the water directly from the water supply pipes and flush the closet bowl provide the best operation and most economical use of water. These valves do away with the flush tank and connections, making a neat, sanitary installation. The valve is opened by a lever which allows the water to enter the closet directly. The closing of the valve is automatic, usually controlled through a by-pass, and regulated by a screw which will determine the period of time the valve is kept open. This regulation should allow the valve to be open no longer than the time required to flush the bowl.

There are many types of flush valves on the market, each having its own special design. A good type of valve is constructed so that it operates on various pressures from 5 to 75 lbs. without requiring regulation of the valve. They also should be so constructed that they cannot be held open for continuous flushing.

The one obstacle in an installation of this type of valve in an ordinary dwelling is that the valve requires at least a $1\frac{1}{4}''$ pipe for its supply. This fact prohibits its installation in dwellings which are connected to the street with a $\frac{3}{4}''$ or $1''$ service pipe.

Faucets. A faucet is a valve controlling the outlet of water from a pipe. The *compression-type* faucet, probably the most widely used in the home, is a faucet which is controlled by a washer which is compressed against a seat by turning a threaded spindle. There are many styles of compression faucets for use on kitchen and bathroom fixtures, but their construction is fundamentally the same.

Fuller-ball Faucet. This type of faucet is not as common as it was a few years ago. Its main feature is rapid operation. It has been replaced by compression faucets, which have a multiple-threaded, spindle screw which affords quick operation with the other advantages of a compression faucet. Fuller faucets shut off the supply of water upon a one quarter turn of the handle, by forcing a soft, acorn-shaped, rubber ball against a cup-shaped seat. Quick action of this faucet is apt to cause serious water hammer. The soft rubber ball does not resist the action of hot water and corrosive liquids as well as the compression-type of faucet washer.

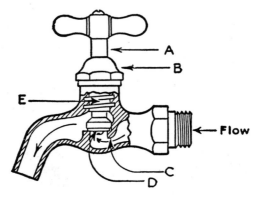

FIG. 4.27. Compression faucet.

A. Spindle; B. cap nut; C. seat; D. composition washer; E. screw.

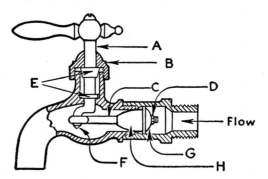

FIG. 4.28. Fuller-ball faucet.

A. Spindle; B. cap nut; C. valve rod; D. adjusting nut; E. spindle guide; F. eccentric; G. Fuller ballcap; H. Fuller ball.

Sill Cock. This is the term applied to a faucet placed near the sill of the house for the purpose of supplying water for a garden hose. This faucet is usually the compression type and has a threaded spout for the purpose of connecting the garden hose.

Special Valves. *Relief Valves.* A hot water storage tank is potential dynamite unless properly protected by a good relief valve. The type of valve that is sealed to relieve at a pressure slightly greater than the working pressure of the tank is preferable.   Relief valves are placed on the pipe line as near the tank as possible.

Copper tanks must also be protected by a vacuum relief valve to prevent collapse.   Hot water occupies more space than cool or cold water.   The cooling, over a wide temperature range, of a tankful of hot water sets up a partial vacuum that strains the comparatively soft copper to the point of failure.

Relief valves are usually set for a pressure about 10 lbs. per sq. in. above street-main pressure in city installations.   With pressure tank systems

FIG. 4.29. Sill cock.
Courtesy Hays
Manufacturing Co.

FIG. 4.30. Hot water line, temperature relief valve for combination temperature and pressure relief.   *Courtesy Stack Heater Co.*

(used in rural systems), these valves are set a few pounds above the maximum *safe* working pressure of the tank.   Vacuum relief valves are usually set for about 7″ of mercury.

Traps and Waste Valves.   The prime purpose of a trap is to prevent the escape of sewer gas into the rooms of the building.   To function properly, a trap must: (a) have a seal deep enough to prevent passage of sewer gas; (b) be vented to prevent passage of sewer gas while waste is flowing, (c) be strong and have smooth interior surfaces to prevent clogging; and (d) have a means of access to its interior for cleaning in case of stoppage.

The most common types of trap are the "P" or the "S" trap which are usually made either of lead, or of brass which may be plain or plated.   Cast iron house traps are used in the drainage system to prevent gas from the sewer main from entering the house drainage system.   The "P" trap is the best type of trap to use for lavatory and sinks, because it can be vented more readily. The "S" trap is not permitted by some plumbing codes, as the vent cannot be connected near the water seal. Some "S" and "P" traps are provided with vents as an integral part of the trap.

Special traps are available for fixtures such as bath tubs, shower stalls, and other fixtures which may drain into the sewage disposal system. Grease

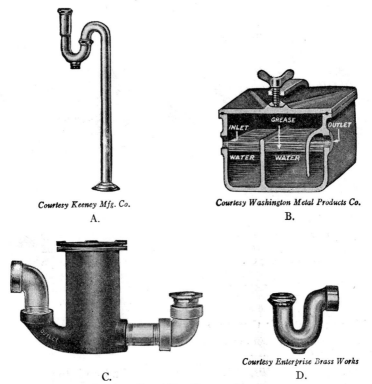

Courtesy Keeney Mfg. Co.
A.

Courtesy Washington Metal Products Co.
B.

Courtesy Enterprise Brass Works
D.

C.

Fig. 4.31.   Common traps.

A._Tubular, "S" trap; B. Grease trap; C. Drum type trap for built-in tub; D. Cast brass "P" type trap.

traps are installed in the drainage system for the purpose of separating grease from waste water, so that large quantities of grease are not discharged into the sewer. Grease traps are not considered necessary for ordinary household use, but in some localities grease traps or catch basins are required.   In cases where a septic tank is used, it is considered economical to install a grease trap.

Waste Valves.   Waste valves are manufactured in many designs for the discharge of the water used in a fixture.   The most common form is the stopper, which is a rubber plug tapered to fit into the opening in the drain. Rubber stopper sizes are determined by the diameter of the opening. Mechanical waste valves are now used in most modern bathroom tubs and basins. These valves are operated without putting the hands in the water to be drained. Adjustment is possible if, after extensive use, the valve does not seat itself properly.

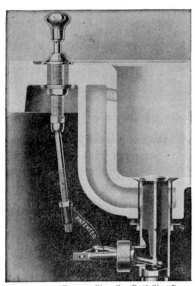

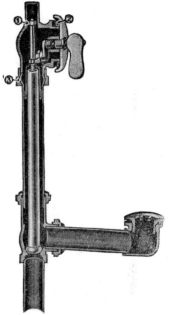

Courtesy Elger Co., Ford City, Pa.

A.

Courtesy Globe Brass Mfg. Co.

B.

Fig. 4.32.   Waste valves.

A. "Pop-Up" waste for basin; B. Lever lift waste for built-in tub.

Fixtures. *Water closets* are usually constructed of vitreous china, the trap being cast as part of the fixture to insure air and watertightness. Most of the domestic types of closets are fastened to the floor and are provided with an inlet for the flush either on the back, top, or side of the fixture. The outlet horn of the closet is connected to the drainage system, usually through a lead "bend." There are many patented closet flanges that provide for this connection. A good type of connection is sealed by an asbestos ring as shown in Fig. 4.33.   The closet is set level on the floor by means of putty, and then the connection is made watertight by clamping the closet to the flange by means of brass closet bolts which have a "T" head that is inserted into the slot in the flange.   The putty should not be used to make the joint between closet and waste.   Putty is necessary only to make an even joint with the floor.

Fɪɢ. 4.33.   Connection sealed by asbestos ring.

Probably the weakest spot in the drainage system is the joint between the closet and the drain pipe.   The importance of this joint cannot be minimized, as the health of the occupants of the house depends upon its tightness.

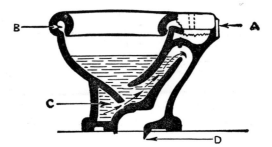

Fɪɢ. 4.34.   Cross section of a siphon jet water closet.

Recently connections for the water closet to the drainage system have been made by fitting the closet with a threaded nipple that screws into a floor coupling which is connected to the soil pipe.   This type of connection usually requires no bolts for closet fastening.

The above illustration shows a cross section of a siphon-jet water closet. The water inlet on the back at *A* is connected to the tank or flush valve by means of a brass tube elbow, or pipe.   When the lever is pulled, water rushes in the inlet at A, and around the flush rim, B, thus washing all parts of the sides of the bowl. Some water is diverted to C, through a by-pass, and it rushes through the jet in the direction of the arrows, causing a siphon action which removes the solid material quickly. After the flush, the water forms a deep seal in the trap, insuring against the entrance of sewer gases into the room. The spud, D, forms the joint with the drainage pipe in the

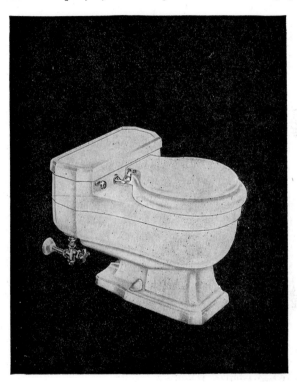

FIG. 4.35. One piece water closet and tank. *Courtesy W. A. Case & Son Mfg. Co.*

floor. As most closets are made of vitreous china, they are self-cleansing to a certain extent, due to the extreme smoothness of the surface. A well designed closet has enough room in the waste for passage of a $2\frac{7}{8}''$ ball. The depth of the seal in the trap should be from $3''$ to $4''$, and the trap usually holds about 3 quarts of water.

In order to have fewer exposed parts around the water closet, the modern fixture is quite often made in one piece with the tank. This design improves the looks of the fixture and makes it possible to keep the fixture clean with a minimum of work.   This type of fixture also provides quieter action than the higher tank or automatic flush valve.

Bathtubs are made in sizes ranging from 4′ to 6′, the most common being 5′6″ in length.   The majority of tubs are made of cast iron with a surface of porcelain enamel that is either white, or colored to match tile or other fixtures.

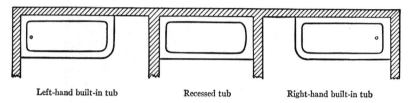

Left-hand built-in tub   Recessed tub   Right-hand built-in tub

Fig. 4.36.   Types of built-in tubs.

Tubs are made in three forms: (a) the roll-rim type on legs, (b) the roll-rim type on pedestal, and (c) the built-in type. Of these three, the

Fig. 4.37.   Concealed combination bath supply and waste fixture. *Courtesy of H. E. Robertson.*

built-in type makes the most satisfactory installation, providing the joint with the floor and wall is inside the wall, so that a crack will not develop as the building settles.   Special hangers are on the market, which act as water seals between walls and edges of built-in tubs or shower receptors. The use of a hanger plus waterproof fittings makes water penetration impossible at this point.   Built-in tubs are made in three general types: (a) to fit in a left-hand corner, (b) to fit in a right-hand corner, or (c) to join the wall on three sides (recessed type). Fittings required for the bathtub are usually supplied with the tub.

There is probably more concealed piping around the bathtub than any of the other fixtures and, for this reason, the installation of pipe fittings and valves of the best quality is the most economical policy.   Mixing valves are usually installed in order to deliver the water into the tub at the proper temperature.   These are usually globe valves which are heavily plated to prevent corrosion. The most desirable installation is the type in which all fittings are concealed except for their handles and spouts.

Shower stalls for use in the bathroom are made by installing a shower receptor and building the walls of tile, marble, or glass. A door, usually of glass with chrome-plated, brass fittings, completes the waterproof compartment, which has a space at the top for ventilation. Shower-bath heads are of various designs and are adjustable so that the direction of the spray can be changed by the user. Some shower baths are installed with a mixing valve that requires only the adjustment of one handle in order to control the temperature of the spray.

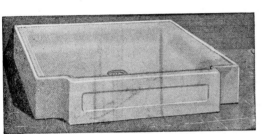

FIG. 4.38. Porcelain enamel shower receptor.

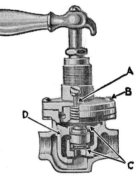

FIG. 4.39. Shower mixing valve.

A. Regulating screw to prevent possible scalding.
B. Faceplate set screws, easily removable with a screwdriver for rewashering.
C. Single stem with a double seat.
D. Removable plug or core.

Lavatories and wash basins are usually made either of cast iron with a porcelain enameled surface, or of vitreous china. The main types of basins are the wall type, the pedestal type, and a combination of both. The wall type is hung on the wall by means of a cast iron hanger, which should be fastened securely to the studding in the wall with screws or lag bolts. The fixture should be so installed that the weight is not supported by the supply pipes or trap.

It is convenient in some washrooms to install corner basins which hang from two adjacent walls. The top of the basin is placed 30″ above the floor. It is the usual practice to install the cold water service on the right on all plumbing fixtures which have a supply of both cold and hot water. Connections between the trap and drain are usually made by the use of slip joints which permit slight movement of the fixture without possible break-age of ridged pipe connections.

Kitchen sinks are probably the most important of the plumbing fixtures, especially in some rural dwellings, where the sink is the first fixture to be installed.   Kitchen sinks are made in several styles: the one-piece sink with drain-board, the steel cabinet sink, and the built-in sink with a tile, or lino-leum drainboard.   Consideration should be given to the proper height of the sink, as it may cause unnecessary stooping if placed too low.   The height, therefore, should be governed wherever possible by the height of the person

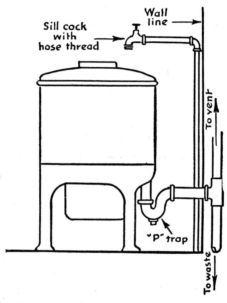

Fɪɢ. 4.40.   Washing machine installed as part of the plumbing system.

who is to use the sink most often.   For the average user 35″ or 36″ above the floor is not too high.   Fittings for the kitchen sink include a mixing faucet which has a movable spout and a basket-type strainer, which can be removed to dispose of larger particles of solid material.

Laundry tubs are usually placed in a separate room.   Sometimes the com-bination sink and laundry tub is used where the dwelling is small.   Tubs are made of glazed clay or stoneware.   Where space is ample, tubs are installed in pairs and may be arranged so that they discharge through the same trap.

Although the *washing machine* is not considered a plumbing fixture, it is advisable in some cases to install supply pipes and faucets for filling the machine, and also to provide for its drainage. Connection with the drainage system should be through a trap, placed as near the machine as practicable. The size of the drain should be at least as large, or larger, than the drain opening in the machine. Where the machine is apt to vibrate a good deal, connection between the trap and machine can be made by a rubber hose, of the type used on automobile cooling systems.

Insulation. Insulation of heating units, connecting pipes, storage tanks, and the distribution pipe lines will result in more satisfactory water temperatures at all times of the year. In practically every installation, the insulation saves its cost in a year or two, by reducing fuel bills. Every heated surface acts like a radiator if it is uninsulated. Hot water supply pipes and boiler or domestic water heaters are not designed to act as house heating units. For this reason the cost of wasted heat from these items is many times greater than the price of the materials and labor that prevent such heat losses.

Plumbing in different parts of the country requires various amounts of protection because of the climate. In the northern sections where extreme cold reaches water pipes even at a depth of 9' below ground, it is necessary to protect both hot and cold water lines. In the extreme south only the hot water lines need to be insulated. Between these extremes lie the general uses of insulation to conserve fuel by covering the hot water generators, hot water storage tanks, and pipe lines with various thicknesses of insulation. It has been found that the heat loss from bare or improperly covered pipes and heaters may amount to 15% or 25% of the total heat. A good covering will save 80% to 95% of the surface losses from bare pipe.

The first requirements of an insulating material are that it be fire-resistant and a poor conductor of heat. These qualities are found in asbestos (fiber, air-cell sheets, or cement), magnesia, mineral wool (or rock wool), spun glass, wool felt, and hair felt. All these materials are manufactured in such a variety of shape, size, thickness, and quality that it is impossible to list more than a few of the most common types for small house use.

The following illustrations show a few of the shapes stocked by most supply houses. Figure 4.41 shows a ready-made cover for storage tanks made of three- or five-ply air-cell board, complete with brass bands to hold it in place, and a small sack of asbestos cement to finish the top and bottom of the tank. Figure 4.42 shows how easily the cover may be applied. Covers for any horizontal tank may be obtained also. As all of these covers are

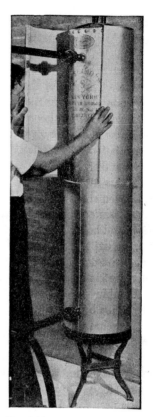

FIG. 4.41. Asbestos tank cover.
Courtesy Hot Stream Heater Co.

FIG. 4.42. Method of applying
insulation.

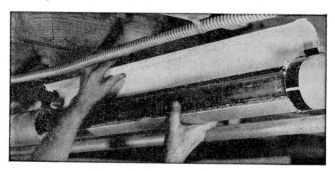

FIG. 4.43. Placing pipe covering around pipe.

made to fit standard tanks, it is only necessary to mention the capacity of the tank when ordering the cover.

Figure 4.43 shows pipe covering being placed around a pipe. The ordinary, corrugated, air-cell type is manufactured in sections 36″ long in hollow cylinders that are split lengthwise. The newer types are finished with stiff asbestos paper, or aluminum foil, which save pasting and present an attractive appearance. The most common type, however, is the canvas covered split tube that requires pasting along a flap to hold it closed around the pipe. All insulation requires straps of metal to make a permanent job.

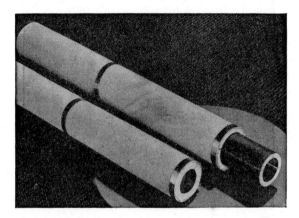

FIG. 4.44.   Special cold water pipe covering.

Special Note: All tubular pipe coverings are listed according to thickness, type of finish, material, and pipe size. Iron pipe is larger than copper tubing of the same size. Thus, insulation for ½″ iron or brass pipe is slightly *larger* in diameter than that required for brass tubing. This annoying practice should be remembered when ordering tubular insulation. Regardless of size, all of these insulations are usually sold by the carton, although the larger sizes, over 2″, are sometimes retailed in broken lots or by the piece.

Figure 4.44 shows a special, cold water pipe covering to keep water cold and to prevent condensation on the pipes with the consequent damage from dripping. This is good insurance when cold water lines run over expensive ceilings, wood paneled walls, or places of public assembly. The inner tube is coated inside and out with asphalt compound.

There is also a pipe covering for protection against ordinary freezing conditions. It is composed of layers of hair felt with a layer of asphalt saturated, wool felt inside. It is used for cold water also.

There is a pipe covering of magnesia that is slightly more costly, but much more efficient than the air-cell type. It is applied like any other tubular insulation.

FIG. 4.45.   Magnesia insulating blocks.

Figure 4.45 shows several magnesia blocks for insulating flat, curved, or irregular surfaces. They are excellent for boiler, heater, or tank insulation. All boilers other than the jacketed type should be insulated with at least 1″, and preferably 1½″ of good insulating material. These blocks, which are 1″ thick, and which are covered with a thick coat of asbestos cement, troweled to a smooth finish, give lasting insulating efficiency. A less effective, but less expensive, insulation may be obtained by applying a coating of asbestos cement 1″ thick, over the surface only.

Figure 4.46 shows the most common method of applying asbestos cement to a boiler. The chicken wire is holding blocks of magnesia in place, while the finished coat of asbestos is being applied. If the blocks are eliminated, a base coat of asphalt cement must be applied before the chicken wire is stretched and fitted around the boiler.

FIG. 4.46.   Applying asbestos cement to boiler.

To estimate the quantity of asbestos cement needed to cover the boiler and pipe fittings, measure the entire surface of the boiler, not including the base where no water circulates. (Openings for doors, pipes, etc., may be disregarded.) A 100 lb. bag of asbestos cement will cover about 20 to 25 sq. ft. of surface to a thickness of 1″. Some brands of cement are sold in 50 lb. paper bags.

One-inch mesh or "chicken wire" is used to reinforce the cement, because asbestos cement has little or no inherent strength to maintain itself in position. The following tools are convenient for measuring and cutting asbestos blocks, and for applying a coating of asbestos to a boiler or heater: steel tape, plasterer's trowel, old hand saw, sharp pocketknife, pliers, tub or platform for mixing cement, and a small pointing trowel.

Mixing and Applying Asbestos Cement on a Boiler. To insure the best results, the boiler should be warm when the cement is applied. This will prevent the formation of large cracks in the coating when the boiler is heated. At least two coats should be applied to boilers and pipe fittings. For the boiler, the first coat should be about 1″ thick and the second coat ½″. The pipe fittings may be covered with two ½″ coats. In all cases, the first coat should be applied with the hands or a plasterer's trowel. Enough pressure should be used to make the cement adhere to the surface, but without "packing." The first surface should be roughened or scratched to form a good bond with the second coat.

The asbestos cement should be mixed in a clean mortar tub or box with just enough clean water to make the mixture workable. The mixture should be stirred until smooth and buttery. All rust and dirt should be cleaned off the boiler, and a final inspection of joints, threads, and fastenings should be made to avoid extra work resulting from leaks. All items, such as gauges, connections, thermostat connections, should be in place on the boiler, so that the insulation may be fitted snugly around them.

Beginning at any convenient point, the moist and plastic asbestos cement is daubed on the boiler. All joints between sections should be filled completely and brought out to the general surface of the boiler coating. Around the doors or openings for the flue pipe or dampers, it is usually better to keep about ½″ away from the opening all around. This prevents breaking of the edges of the coating as the doors are opened.

When the first coat is fairly dry, the wire reinforcement should be stretched and fitted to hold the first coat in place. The netting may be wrapped around the boiler snugly, and holes cut for all openings. Small pieces of the mesh may be bent and wired firmly in place over curved or irregular surfaces. Both coats are reinforced by the wire mesh, after it becomes embedded between them. After the first coat is dry, cracks may appear. These are covered and filled in by the second coat.

Magnesia cement is not recommended as a finishing cement, although its insulating efficiency is high. Sometimes a small amount of Portland cement is added to give the asbestos finishing cement a harder finish. While the second coat is still moist, the thickness of the two coats may be tested by driving the point of a sharp knife into the asbestos until it hits the metal. The moist asbestos will mark the knife, so that it may be measured for the desired thickness of covering.

After the entire coating has had time to dry thoroughly, it may be painted or given a coat of shellac. Aluminum paint is especially long wearing and attractive in appearance. The doors and uncovered base should be painted gray or black, with a narrow band of the same color around the edges of the insulation near the openings.

Insulating Pipes. Hot air furnaces and pipes should be covered with corrugated asbestos paper held firmly in place with bands or wire. The paper comes in rolls about 37" wide, containing approximately 250 sq. ft. Two or three layers of this paper give excellent insulation against excessive heat losses.

If the top of the hot air furnace is cupped, it can be leveled up with sand, and then three or four flat disks of asbestos paper laid over it. These pieces may be held in place by extending the asbestos cement covering of the sloping part of the top of the furnace, until it plasters down the edges securely.

Covering Pipes and Fittings. Covering water pipes and fittings with tubular insulation is very simple. To estimate the quantity needed, measure the distance between fittings on all pipes to be covered and combine the measurements. The fittings, valve bodies, sharp curves, etc., should be covered with asbestos cement, molded to the shape of the fitting. The total number of pieces necessary for a particular size of pipe may be obtained by dividing the total length by three. Metal band fastenings are furnished with the covering.

For pasting the canvas flaps on air-cell coverings, or for fastening asbestos paper around large hot air pipes or ducts, a suitable paste is sold in powdered form by manufacturers of insulating materials.

A satisfactory paste, similar to that used for hanging paper, may be made of flour and water. Mix 1 part of powdered alum with 50 parts of sifted white flour, and add enough *cold* water to make a smooth paste. Mix thoroughly to prevent lumps and add boiling water until the paste begins to thicken. Thick or thin paste is determined by the amount of water added. Cold water only should be used and the paste cooked to the desired consistency. Flour paste becomes moldy and useless if allowed to stand for any great length of time.

All pipes should be clean and in good condition before covering. The tubular sections should be opened carefully, and the canvas flaps loosened.

Paste may be applied to the flap before or after the section has been fitted around the pipe. Each section, open side up, is slipped around the pipe and pressed tightly together to close the seam. The flap over the split is pasted generously and pulled around the section to form a smooth, tight joint. The canvas overlap at one end of the section is pulled out, so that each section may join tightly with the next section. The joint between the two is sealed by pasting the overlaps. The straight lengths of pipe between fittings are covered in this manner. When small sections are needed, the tubing can be cut easily with a sharp knife or a saw. It is the usual practice to cover the straight sections first, and then to fill in the spaces for joints, fittings, valves, with asbestos cement.

All metal bands should be applied around the pipe covering after all the other work is completed to give a clean and neat appearance to the job. The bands should be placed about 18″ apart, over joints and midway between them. By using pliers, the bands may be pulled up tightly like a belt and fastened securely. In the absence of metal bands, loops of wire may be used, but care must be taken to prevent cutting into the canvas cover on the tubing as the wire is twisted tight.

It should be obvious that in new construction the insulating work must be done before the lath and plaster work is begun. Where pipes run in exterior walls that are insulated with loose granular insulation, it is not necessary to cover the pipes with the tubing insulation. Pipes under porches, or other places exposed to dampness or dripping water, should be protected against such a condition by hanging shields of metal, so that water will not drip directly upon the covering.

Cesspools. When a city or town sewer is not available for connection to the house sewer, a means of disposal must be provided. "Leaching" cesspools are probably the most common types of pit used for the reception and detention of sewage. In places where the ground is well drained, and where houses are not too congested, this type of disposal is not objectionable.

In anticipation of the construction an important consideration is the location of the cesspool, which usually is placed about 15′ or 20′ from the house, and in such a location that surface water will not easily enter it during a rain storm. For an ordinary dwelling a hole 7′ in diameter and about the same depth is sufficient. A trench is also dug from the house to the cesspool. The amount of pitch necessary, using a 4″ glazed drain tile with cemented joints, is about 1′ in 20′. Too much pitch may cause solid matter to accumulate in the pipe, which depends on a full charge to float the solids and scour the joints. A drainage pipe must not be too large because too large a pipe will not flush itself.

Cesspools are made of stone, brick, wood, or concrete blocks. Stone is a good material where it is available. No mortar is used as the openings are left for drainage purposes. Brick is "laid up" in much the same way as stone. Near the top, usually, the bricks are set in mortar to avoid possible collapse. Wood may be used but is not permanent. Concrete cesspool blocks are made in a curved form, have an interlocking end, and a hole in the side for seepage. These blocks are inexpensive and provide satisfactory construction.

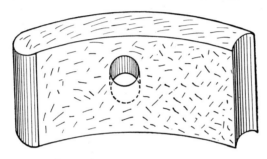

Fig. 4.47.   Concrete cesspool block.

As the wall of the cesspool is being laid up, provision for the entrance of the sewer pipe is made and, near the top, the diameter is decreased by leaving out several bricks from each successive tier. At the top, a stone, concrete, or steel cover is provided, usually just below the surface of the ground.

After many years of service, or due to improper drainage of the soil near the cesspool, it may be necessary to build a second cesspool or overflow to take care of the liquid which will not disperse in the ground from the first. This is built in the same manner as the first cesspool. A trench is dug, and a drain pipe is placed in the first cesspool at a point lower than the house drain. Proper pitch is given the drain, and entrance is provided for it in the second cesspool. In a system of this type, the first cesspool acts as a trap for grease and solid materials, and the second is a means of draining the liquids. If possible, the cesspool should be surrounded by a jacket of sand to filter its contents, as they seep away.

Septic Tanks. A more satisfactory method for the disposal of sewage is by the use of the septic tank. The septic tank differs from the cesspool in

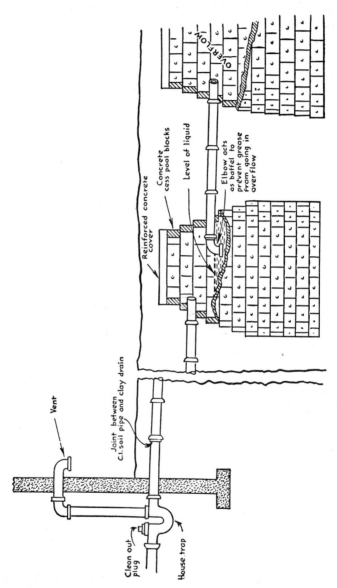

FIG. 4.48.   Diagram of cesspool and overflow.

that the cesspool holds the solids of sewage and drains the liquid until the soil becomes clogged.   The septic tank is a specially designed tank in which natural bacterial action changes the solids to liquid.   Final disposal is then easier, safer, and less liable to service troubles.

One common method of disposal of the liquid or effluent discharge from the septic tank is by means of an underground system of loose-jointed tile pipes laid in sandy soil at about 18″ below the surface, depending on local conditions.

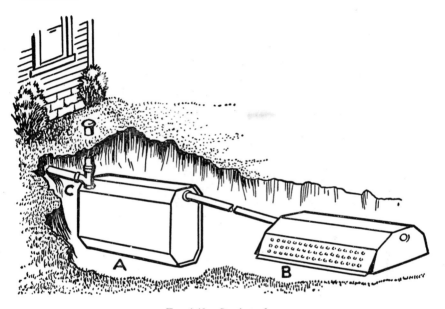

FIG. 4.49.   Septic tank.

Septic tanks, like cesspools, are built of brick, concrete, or masonry. Metal septic tanks are also in use and, because of ease and convenience in installing, and due to improvements in manufacture, are rapidly increasing in the public favor.

A highly popular type of septic tank is that shown in Fig. 4.49.   The septic tank A receives the sewage from the house through the house drain C. Instead of a distributing field of tile, a special drain pool B is provided.   This pool, as well as the septic tank, is made of No. 14 gauge, or heavier, copper-bearing steel, heavily coated inside and out with mineral asphalt, melted on at a high temperature, for protection against the corrosive action of moisture, acids, and soil. All seams are electrically welded. The intake opening is designed to take a 4″ (cast-iron or tile) sanitary "T" fitting. The outlet opening has a set-in collar.

Probably 90% of the trouble with septic tank installations is caused by inadequate or poor drainage areas. Interruption in service, and expense of digging up lawns and drainage areas, will be largely avoided if proper drainage is provided. The drain pool as illustrated in Fig. 4.49 has been developed as a standard plan of drainage suitable for most installations. Its use, instead of home-built cesspools, is recommended. Perforations at the sides, plus the open bottom, provide a larger seepage area than the ordinary

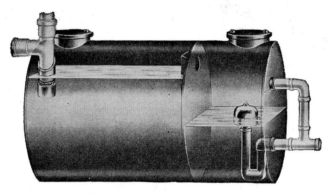

FIG. 4.50. Septic tank with siphon discharge.

leaching pool. Drainage is kept nearer the surface of the ground where soil conditions are usually best for final disposal. Two or more pools can be installed to provide sufficient drainage when necessary.

Filter beds of drain tile laid in trenches are also satisfactory, if provided in adequate amount and laid under careful supervision.

For ordinary home use, a minimum tank capacity of 50 gallons per person, or a total size of 300 gallons is recommended by many leading authorities. For other than home installations, the tank capacity should be equal to the number of gallons of water likely to be used over a 24 hour period.

The septic tank also cares for the kitchen waste in ordinary home use. For restaurants, hotels, and farms, or installations where large amounts of grease are present, a grease trap should be installed on the kitchen waste or drain line.

An improved septic tank with a built-in siphon discharge unit is illustrated by Fig. 4.50. The built-in siphon ensures intermittent discharge considered essential to allow the sewage to work off in the soil, and to permit air to enter the soil spaces before another discharge is received from the septic tank. The siphon of this two-chamber septic tank discharges at 4 to 8 hour intervals in sufficient volume to distribute the effluent equally over the entire filter field.

Chapter 2

~~~~~~

TOOLS USED IN PLUMBING WORK

Tools for Cutting and Threading Pipe: The Vise, The Pipe Cutter, The Pipe Reamer, Pipe Dies, Pipe Tap, Pipe Wrenches . . . Tools for Cast-Iron Soil Pipe: Fire Pot, Blow Torch, Machinist's Hammer, Joint-runner, Chisels, Caulking Irons, Plumb Bob, Testing Plugs . . . Miscellaneous Plumbing Tools: Brass Pipe Tools, Copper Tube Cutter, Bending Springs, Flaring Tool, Closet Auger, Sewer Auger, Plunger, Bibb Seat Dresser

It would be impracticable for the home owner to have a full set of plumber's tools. However, the man who has a home workshop will usually provide himself with the more important plumbing tools needed to supplement his woodworking and metalworking tools so that he will be able to do a number of practical plumbing repair jobs in his home. In this discussion of plumbing tools, those used in cutting, threading, and fitting threaded pipe will be considered first, then special tools for cast-iron drain pipe and, finally, miscellaneous tools. A complete set of plumbing tools represents an investment of several hundred dollars; therefore, it is usually a question of which tools are most necessary, and which tools can be overlooked. The type of work will govern the selection of tools for the tool kit. If the supply pipes of the home are made up with screwed fittings, standard dies and pipe cutters are essential, while they would be of little use in a home where copper tube is used throughout.

Tools for Cutting and Threading Pipe. *Vise.* A pipe vise is absolutely necessary for plumbing work. The bench-type pipe vise is constructed so that the frame can be opened quickly for releasing the pipe after it is threaded. The chain pipe vise is less awkward and takes up less space on the bench. It might be a good investment to install a combination machinist's and pipe vise which can be used for all-around work in the home workshop.

Pipe Cutter. A pipe cutter cuts lengths of pipe quickly and neatly. If there is not much pipe to be cut a hacksaw may be substituted. However, where a number of pieces are to be cut, a pipe cutter will save considerable time, and it has the further advantage of making a clean, square cut on the end of the pipe. If a saw is used, much more care must be taken to obtain a square cut, which is essential for starting the pipe die.

Pipe Reamer. Pipe cutters leave burrs inside the cut end of a pipe, which diminish the cross-sectional area of the opening of the pipe and thus

FIG. 4.51. Pipe vise. *Courtesy Armstrong Manufacturing Co.*

FIG. 4.52. Chain type pipe vise.

FIG. 4.53. Combination machinist's and pipe vise.

impair the flow through the pipe. These burrs must be removed by a burring reamer, which leaves the pipe joint with a slightly beveled edge. The reamer is inserted in an ordinary carpenter's brace.

Pipe Dies. Pipe dies are used for putting the thread on the end of pipe, so that the pipe may be joined to the fitting. A pipe die is held in a die stock, which is fitted with a guide bushing of the proper size. For the amateur, a set of pipe dies ranging from ⅛″ to 1″ in diameter will do most of the work required. Dies for cutting larger threads are usually included in the larger sets, which are necessarily more expensive. Solid dies are made in one piece and are nonadjustable, while split or adjustable dies can be

Fig. 4.54. Drop forged pipe cutter.
Courtesy Armstrong Manufacturing Co.

Fig. 4.55. Pipe reamer.
*Courtesy Armstrong
Manufacturing Co.*

adjusted for wear and for meeting irregularities in pipe fittings. Pipe dies are made with either right-hand or left-hand threads; however, unless otherwise stated, they are always understood to be right-handed. They are

Fig. 4.56. Pipe stock and die.
Courtesy Armstrong Manufacturing Co.

designed to cut the American National Thread, which is the standard pipe thread used in this country.

Pipe Tap. A pipe tap is used for making internal pipe threads. Taps are marked on the shank to show the diameter of the pipe thread and the

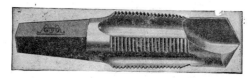

Fig. 4.57. Combined drill and tap.

number of threads per inch which the tap cuts. Sizes refer to the nominal diameter of the pipe, and not to the actual diameter of the tap. In order to use a tap properly, a tap hole must first be drilled in the material. The diameter of the tap drill for any given tap is found in the following table:

TABLE 1. TAP DRILL SIZES FOR AMERICAN NATIONAL PIPE THREADS

Nominal Size of Pipe	Threads per Inch	Tap Drill Size
⅛″	27	11/32″
¼″	18	7/16″
⅜″	18	37/64″
½″	14	23/32″
¾″	14	59/64″
1″	11½	15/32″
1¼″	11½	1½″
1½″	11½	147/64″
2″	11½	27/32″

Pipe Wrenches. A set of wrenches is a prime necessity for all pipe fitting. There is a proper size for every purpose that enables the mechanic to do the

FIG. 4.58. Monkey wrench. *Courtesy J. H. Williams Co.*

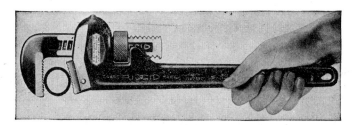

FIG. 4.59. Pipe wrench.

job quickly without damage to the work. The monkey wrench should be used on nuts, valves, and unions where it may be fitted to flat parallel surfaces. It should be placed in position and then fitted by turning the adjustment screw until the jaws grip firmly as the handle is moved. The Stillson wrench is used for pipes that have no special surface finish which might be scarred. It should be slipped over the pipe loosely and the jaws closed gradually by the adjustment nut until the teeth in the jaws just grip the pipe when the handle is moved. Further tightening will tend to crush the pipe. The chain wrench, or chain tongs as it is sometimes called, is used only on the larger sizes of threaded pipe. The strap wrench is used in making up brass- or chromium-plated pipe and fittings. The strap wraps around the pipe and builds up enough friction to turn the threads

FIG. 4.60.   Strap wrench.

into fittings without marring finished surfaces. Spud and basin wrenches are nonadjustable end wrenches and are most convenient for tightening the locknuts on the basin faucet and closet bowl. A pair of slip-joint pliers may be used instead of a basin wrench.

TABLE 2.   TABLE OF WRENCH SIZES FOR STANDARD PIPE

Size of Pipe	Size of Wrench
⅛″–¼″ pipe	6″ wrench
⅜″–½″ pipe	10″ wrench
¾″ pipe	14″ wrench
1″–1¼″ pipe	18″ wrench
1½″–2″ pipe	24″ wrench
larger sizes	36″ wrench or chain tongs

Hacksaw. The hacksaw with an adjustable frame is very convenient for cutting pipe or tubing. The blade must be placed in the frame so that the teeth point forward, because the cutting is done only on the forward stroke. For iron or brass pipe, a saw blade with 24 teeth per inch is necessary. For conduit and other thin tubing, a saw blade with 32 teeth per inch is recommended

Tools for Cast-Iron Soil Pipe. *Fire Pot.* A gasoline fire pot is a necessity when doing soil pipe work. Being portable, it may be used near the job and therefore is more convenient than a gas furnace. It is used to melt lead and also to heat soldering irons.

Blow Torch. A gasoline blow torch is especially useful in melting out lead joints. It can also be used for heating soldering irons and is indispensable in making soldered joints on copper tubing.

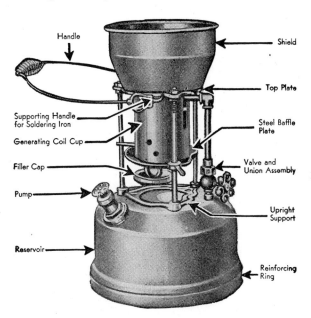

Handle

Shield

Top Plate

Supporting Handle for Soldering Iron

Steel Baffle Plate

Generating Coil Cup

Filler Cap

Valve and Union Assembly

Pump

Upright Support

Reservoir

Reinforcing Ring

FIG. 4.61.   Gasoline fire pot.

The Care and Use of a Fire Pot and Blow Torch. The fire pot and blow torch are much the same in their operation but differ in size. Like any other tool, a blow torch or fire pot is safe when used with care. In their operation, air pressure forces gasoline into the generating coil or chamber, which is kept hot enough to vaporize the gasoline. The resulting gas is forced through a small opening which, by its drop in pressure, draws in a sufficient amount of air to form a combustible mixture.

To fill the torch, remove the filler plug and fill the reservoir with white gasoline. *Caution: For safety do this outdoors in open air!* To obtain pressure, close the valve, unscrew pump plunger, and pump up air pressure. To start the torch, hold the hand over the coil or combustion chamber and turn on the valve. This will allow gasoline to drip into drip or coil cup. (Alcohol may be used to fill the cup for preheating. Alcohol will burn with a cleaner flame than gasoline.) Light the gasoline in the drip cup. This will preheat the gasoline in the coil or chamber, causing it to vaporize. Before the gasoline is burned up, turn on the valve allowing the flame from the cup to ignite the vapor. *Caution: Turn the valve slowly as there may*

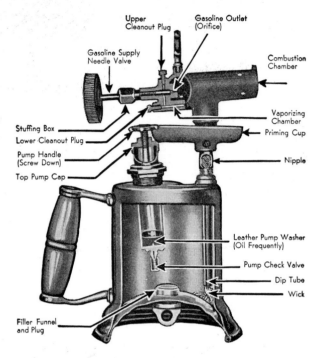

Upper
Cleanout Plug

Gasoline Outlet
(Orifice)

Gasoline Supply
Needle Valve

Combustion
Chamber

Stuffing Box

Lower Cleanout Plug

Pump Handle
(Screw Down)

Top Pump Cap

Vaporizing
Chamber

Priming Cup

Nipple

Leather Pump Washer
(Oil Frequently)

Pump Check Valve

Dip Tube

Wick

Filler Funnel
and Plug

FIG. 4.62.   Cross-sectional view of a blow torch.

not be enough heat to vaporize the gasoline.   If there is not enough heat, re-peat the above operations after flame has completely burned out.   It is a good plan to let all the air out of the chamber by opening the valve after shutting off the torch.

A solder pot, ladle, and pot hook go with the fire pot to handle the molten metal.   A pot 6″ in diameter holds about 18 lbs. of lead, which is enough for average work.   A 4″ diameter ladle will pick up about 4 lbs. of lead, which is enough for pouring a joint in 4″ soil pipe.

The *machinist's hammer* is used for cutting cast-iron pipe and also for general work.   A hammer about 1½ lbs. in weight is good for average work.   For caulking and drilling, a heavier hammer is more convenient.

A *joint-runner* is used close to the open space between the hub and spigot while molten lead is poured into a joint, in a horizontal run of soil pipe. It is also called a "snake" or "running rope" in some localities. Figure 4.63 shows an asbestos, lead joint-runner, held properly in place with a spring clamp, on the spigot end of a cast-iron drain pipe joint. Large pipes require longer runners. The most convenient runner is No. 2, because it can be used on pipes up to 6″ in diameter.

FIG. 4.63.   Joint runner.   IG. 4.64.   Caulking irons.

Chisels. The *cold* chisel is used for cutting cold metal such as C.I. soil pipe. A ¾″ chisel is a good size for general work. The *cape* chisel has a very narrow cutting edge. It may be used to cut narrow grooves or to start a cut on cast iron. The *picking* chisel is the most convenient tool for picking out caulked lead joints that must be replaced because of defects or changes in the line of pipe. It has a flattened blade about 3″ long, as shown in the illustration. A *brick* chisel is indispensable for cutting through brick or stone work. It is used with a heavy hammer. A *floor* chisel has a wide blade, sharpened like a wood chisel, so that it can cut through wood flooring without splitting the floor boards. It is used to cut off the tongues of tongue-and-groove flooring, so that just enough flooring may be removed to permit working between floor beams. After the work has been completed, the pieces may be nailed back in place.

Caulking Irons. Various shapes and sizes are available for caulking oakum and lead into the joints of cast-iron pipe.

The *Plumb Bob.* An extremely handy device. A piece of strong line such as fish line should be used with it. Whenever it is necessary to check the position of holes in flooring in relation to pipe lines, fixtures, or vertical runs, the plumb bob is strung up and used as a guide.

Testing Plugs. After a complete hook-up has been installed, but before it is accepted or used, it should be tested for leaks, cracked hubs, or any other breaks that would cause trouble. The usual method is to close all

FIG. 4.65. Test plugs.

openings except the highest one in the whole system, and then fill the pipes with water. The pressure thus produced will cause leaks at any weak or faulty joints, and these may be caulked or plugged at once. The most convenient means of sealing pipe openings is by the use of test plugs, several of which are shown in their correct position in Fig. 4.65. A test plug has a wide rubber ring set between two metal disks that can be squeezed together by a threaded stem. When the disks are drawn together, the rubber ring expands until it is wedged into the pipe so tightly that no water can pass it.

FIG. 4.66. Jig for holding and cutting copper tubing.

Miscellaneous Plumbing Tools. *Brass Pipe Tools.* While there are special wrenches, cutters, and dies which are manufactured for holding, cutting, and threading brass pipe, they are not an absolute necessity if one has ordinary pipe tools. Brass pipe is finished with a smooth surface on the outside of the pipe and, if it is desirable not to mar this surface, friction vises and wrenches must be used when holding and cutting brass pipe. As the cutting action required for brass is different from that required for steel, special tools for cutting, reaming, and threading brass pipe are available. These tools do a better job than tools designed for steel pipe; however, they should only be used on brass, as they will not stand up if used on steel pipe.

A *jig* for holding and guiding the hacksaw when cutting copper tubing is desirable, if considerable work is to be done with this material.

Copper Tube Cutter. A special, wheel-type cutter for copper tubing is available, which is equipped with a reamer attached to the body. This tool is designed only for copper tubing and not for iron or brass pipe.

FIG. 4.67.   Bending spring.

FIG. 4.68.   Flaring tool. *Courtesy Armstrong Manufacturing Co.*

Bending Springs. When soft copper tubing is bent without some sort of a jig, it tends to collapse and cannot be used without retarding the flow of water through the pipe. A bending spring of the proper size may be

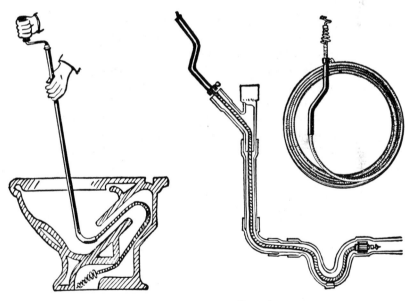

FIG. 4.69.   Closet auger.   FIG. 4.70.   Sewer auger.

placed over the tube and the tube bent by hand to any angle without collapsing the tube. Springs are available for tubing size up to 1″ in diameter.

Flaring Tool. When using copper tube with the flanged-type fittings, a flaring tool is necessary to form the end of the pipe to provide the union.

The tool is held in the end of the pipe and hit with a hammer until the required flange is obtained.

Closet Auger. A closet auger is a handy tool for removing obstructions in a closet bowl. A flexible cable of spring steel is fitted with an auger-shaped wire at one end and a crank handle at the other. A brass tube acts as a guide and holds the cable while the crank is turned. The auger is placed in the bowl and "snaked" through the trap by turning the crank. When the screw-top spring hits the obstruction, it will tend to catch it and thus clear the trap. See Fig. 4.69.

Sewer augers are similar to the closet augers but are larger in diameter and longer. They may be obtained from 6′ to 50′ in length for cleaning drain and sewer pipes. After its use, the auger should be washed well and oiled to prevent rust. See Fig. 4.70.

Fig. 4.71. Plunger.

Plunger. A plunger or "plumber's friend" is useful for forcing an obstruction through a drain pipe or trap. If the trap or drain is filled with water and the plunger is inserted over the drain and pumped, the force of the water will probably loosen and remove the obstruction. This tool may be used on any drain, including the closet bowl.

Bibb Seat Dresser. This is a tool used to resurface the seat of basin faucets, sill cocks, and compression valves, when they are worn so badly that a new washer will not stop the leak. The seat dresser is placed on the faucet, and its handle is turned, thus dressing the seat of the valve. The action of the dresser is much like that of a file. Care must be taken to dress off just enough material to remove the cause of the leak.

Chapter 3

PIPE MEASURING, CUTTING, THREADING, AND INSTALLATION

Methods of Pipe Measurement ... Pipe Cutting ... Pipe Threading ... Making Up Pipe Work ... Typical Piping Installation, A Hot Water Heating System ... Cutting and Assembling Copper Tubes with Solder Fittings ... Joining Copper Tubes with Flared Tube Fittings, Connecting Cast-Iron Pipe, Melting Out Joints in a Run of Cast-Iron Soil Pipe, Melting Lead for Use in Caulking

When making a new installation, it is a good plan to make a diagram of the entire system before the pipe is cut and threaded. All the measurements should be shown on this diagram.

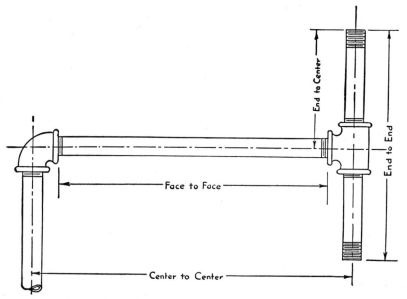

FIG. 4.72. Methods of pipe measurement.

Probably the best method of measuring in pipe work is the center-to-center method. If this method is used, many measurements can be taken

57

at one time. Other methods commonly used for measuring pipe are the end-to-end method, the end-to-center method, and the face-to-face method.

Methods of Pipe Measurement. In order to convert nominal measurements (which are measurements as taken) into the actual lengths of pipe to be cut, the following tables are useful:

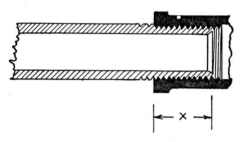

FIG. 4.73. See Table 1.

TABLE 1. DISTANCE A PIPE WILL SCREW INTO VALVES OR FITTINGS

Size of Pipe	Distance Pipe is Screwed into Fittings
⅛″	¼″
¼″	⅜″
⅜″	⅜″
½″	½″
¾″	½″
1″	⁹⁄₁₆″
1¼″	⅝″
1½″	⅝″
2″	¹¹⁄₁₆″

Pipe Cutting. Good results in threading pipe depend largely upon good pipe cutting. Wrought iron, galvanized iron, and brass pipe are cut by means of a pipe cutter. In using this tool, the first cut should be slight, in order to ensure that the starting channel is square with the axis of the pipe, as shown in Fig. 4.75. In order to start cutting on the right track, it is most important that the cutting wheel be sharp. A dull cutting wheel often throws the cutter out of alignment, and the poor cut that results will make it difficult to start the die properly, when threading.

Procedure in Cutting a Length of Pipe:

1. Be sure measurements are correct and that the proper allowance has

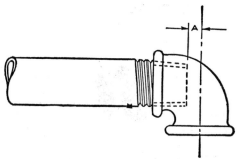

Fig. 4.74. See Table 2.

TABLE 2. DISTANCE FROM THE END OF THE PIPE TO THE CENTER OF THE FITTING

Size of Pi	Dimension A (For 90° "L," "Tee" or Street "L")
½"	⅝"
¾"	13⁄16"
1"	⅞"
1¼"	1⅛"
1½"	1 5⁄16"
2"	1 9⁄16"

been made for the portion of the pipe that is to be screwed into the fittings. (See preceding section.)

2. Place the pipe in the pipe vise, so that the measurement mark extends far enough from the vise so that the cutter will clear the end of the bench.

3. Screw the handle of the cutter until the rollers are firmly resting on the pipe and set the cutting wheel on the mark.

4. Rotate the cutter around the pipe with a slight pressure on rollers, so that the first cut starts a slight channel which is square.

5. Squirt a generous amount of cutting oil over the pipe and cutting wheel. Rotate the cutter about one half turn and screw the handle in to take a deeper cut. Continue until the pipe is cut off.

6. While the pipe is still in the vise, ream with a pipe reamer the burr left by the cutter.

Pipe Threading. The pipe is now ready to be threaded. Clean-cut threads on pipe are necessary for perfect meshing with the threads in the pipe fitting.

Standard Pipe Thread. In this country, pipe and pipe fittings are threaded with the American Standard pipe thread. The specifications for this type of thread are shown in Fig. 4.77.

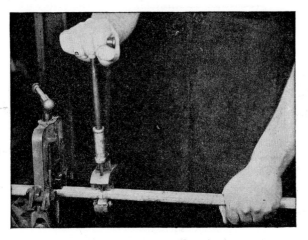

Fig. 4.75.   Cutting pipe with a pipe cutter.

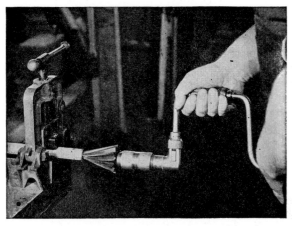

Fig. 4.76.   Pipe reaming.

The thread has an angle of 60°, and it is flattened at the crest and root by an amount equal to .33P. The depth of the thread is therefore .80P. The taper of the thread is 1 in 16, measured on the diameter, which is ¾″ per foot.

The Pipe Stock and Die. There are many types of pipe stocks and dies, each of which has its advantage. For threading pipe under 1″ in diameter, the solid type, which is nonadjustable, and the adjustable type, which is made in two parts that are clamped to the stock with provision for adjustment, are most common. The latter type is most satisfactory.

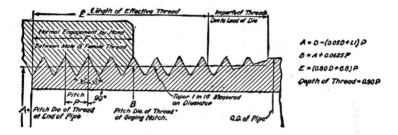

Fig. 4.77. Diagram of Standard pipe thread.

In order to start the die as squarely as possible, a guide bushing is provided for each size of pipe. This bushing fits over the outside of the pipe and helps to start the die straight. The die is made so that the first few threads are cut only to part of the full thread depth. This is the starting side of the die. Adjustable dies have an index mark, which lines up with a corresponding mark on the stock, when the die is in its normal position. If adjustment is necessary in order to obtain a tighter fit, the two parts of the die must be adjusted equally.

It will be noticed from Table 1, Chapter 2, that sizes 1″, 1¼″, 1½″, and 2″ are standardized with 11½ threads per inch. Larger sizes of pipe, 2½″ and above, are made with 8 threads per inch. Stocks for 1″ pipe and larger sizes are difficult to start at the end of the pipe and are apt to make a crooked thread unless guided carefully. A stock which has a mechanism for leading the dies over the pipe at the proper pitch may be used to advantage on sizes from 1″ to 2″. Some stocks for these sizes are made so that one set of dies will cut all sizes in the 11½ thread-per-inch range. The proper taper for the pipe thread is obtained on these sizes by a receding mechanism, which allows the dies at the beginning of the operation to cut the full depth and, as the dies progress, they recede at the proper taper, so that the last few threads grow progressively shallower.

As the average home owner seldom finds any need for threading pipes more than 1″ in diameter, it is recommended that a plumber be called for this work. In some communities, large pipe may be cut and threaded to any required dimensions at the local hardware store.

Procedure in Threading a Pipe:

1. Select the proper dies and guide bushing for the size of pipe to be threaded.

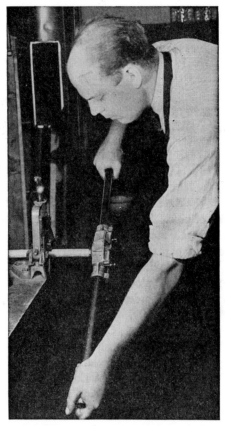

FIG. 4.78. A leakproof joint is the result of clean-cut threads on both the pipe and on the fitting.

2. Place the pipe in the pipe vise, and file a slight chamfer on the end of the pipe for easy starting.

3. Squirt a generous amount of cutting oil over the die and start the thread by turning the stock slowly in a clockwise direction, keeping the dies pressed firmly against the pipe.

4. After the dies have "caught" on the pipe, continue turning the stock, backing it off about one quarter turn after every half turn, in order to break off chips. Continue to apply cutting oil.

5. To determine the correct length of thread, make up a new fitting on the thread being cut, and refer to Table 2, to find the length of pipe thread which should be engaged in the fitting.

6. Examine the thread for defects, being especially careful to make sure that it is straight. Crooked threads are commonly caused by pipe that was not cut square at the end. Chipped threads are often the result of a dull cutter, which should be replaced.

Fig. 4.79. Making up a tee on the end of a length of pipe.

Making Up Pipe Work. After the pipe is cut, reamed, and threaded, it is ready to be made up in sections to form a part of the plumbing system. Theoretically, pipe joints are leak proof, due to the action of the screw and taper on the male thread as it meshes with the tapered female thread in the fitting. This, however, is not always the case in practice, as threading tools become worn in use and do not cut perfect threads. Therefore, it is necessary in practice to use a pipe joint compound, which will fill any small space in the joint where leaking might occur. Any commercial compound may be used. Red lead or white lead, in the ordinary paste form, may be used to make tight joints. In applying any of these materials, spread it on the external thread only, because if used on the fitting, it may cause trouble in the system or impair the flow of water to some extent.

While the pipe is still in the vise, after threading, screw the fitting onto the threaded end. Use a Stillson wrench of the proper size, applying it to the fitting. Remember that the pipe thread is tapered, and too much pressure will cause the fitting to crack. A fitting that is properly made up on pipe, will leave a portion of the thread on the pipe exposed.

It is a good plan to place the wrench on the inside shoulder of the fitting which is beaded. If the wrench should be applied to the outside shoulder

Fig. 4.80.   Correct method of tightening union.

of the fitting, distortion might be caused, which would result in a leaking joint. If it is ever necessary to apply the wrench to the outside shoulder of a fitting, screw a short nipple into that part of the fitting, to keep the distortion to a minimum.

After the make-up of a new section of pipe is complete, it is necessary to connect it to the main line or, in some cases, to the fixture which is being installed. To make this last connection, a pipe union is generally used. The union parts are first made up on the pipe itself, in the same manner as the pipe fittings. The pipes which are being joined should be in perfect alignment at this point. The union seat is set, and the union nut is screwed on by hand. To tighten a union nut, use two wrenches, one to hold the union from turning, while pressure is applied by the other to the union nut. Some unions are not made with a brass seat, but they are kept watertight by means of a fiber gasket. These unions are not as efficient as those with a brass seat, as it is necessary to replace the gasket each time the union is opened. It is suggested that these unions be replaced, wherever possible.

In some gas and steam pipe lines, a left- and right-hand coupling is used instead of the union. This type of joint has the advantage of being more nearly leakproof and eliminates the cost of the union. Such a connection, however, requires a special die for cutting the left-hand thread. Fittings for pipe railings also use left-hand threads. With them it is possible to make up a job of this type without the use of unions. (A left-hand thread is one which will advance when the pipe or fitting is turned in a counterclockwise direction.)

Before turning on the water in a new installation, or in a section which has been repaired, check to see that there is no opening in the system. Then, after the water is turned on, inspect each joint for leakage and repair any leaks by re-threading the pipe provided, of course, that the joint has been properly tightened and that the fitting is in good condition. Do not try to stop leaks by screwing pipe into fittings too far.

Typical Piping Installation. *A Hot Water Heating System.* In order to explain how the operations of measuring, cutting, and threading pipe are applied, a typical piping installation will be described, namely, the installation of a hot water heating system.

The inner tube is first screwed into the boiler union A, and the union and tube are screwed into the 1″ opening at the top of the boiler. The boiler stand E is screwed into the 1″ opening at the bottom of the boiler, and the faucet F is screwed into the stand, providing a means of draining the boiler for cleaning, or of emptying the hot water piping (Fig. 4.81).

The tank and the heating furnace are now placed into position on the floor and, by the use of a long stick, the distance from the face of the coupling G on the hot water line to the center of the boiler outlet at B is measured. This measurement is found to be 7′ 2″. As an elbow B_1 is to be used, Table 2 may be consulted to determine the distance from the end of the pipe to the center of the elbow. For ½″ pipe, this distance is ⅝″. Table 1 is used to determine the length of pipe which is to be screwed into the coupling G. It is found to be ½″. This ½″ is added to the measurement, and the ⅝″ is subtracted, which gives the actual length of pipe to be cut which is 7′ 1⅛″.

The cold water line is to have a valve near the storage tank, in order to shut off the hot water to the house, and it is also to have a tee at the tank, which is to receive a safety valve. A short piece of pipe, or a nipple, can be used to assemble the valve and tee. The assembled valve, nipple, and tee are now made up on a long piece of pipe, and the measurement is taken in the following way: With the stick, measure the distance from the center of the inlet hole A to the face of the cold water coupling G_1. This measure-

STORAGE TANK HOOK-UP

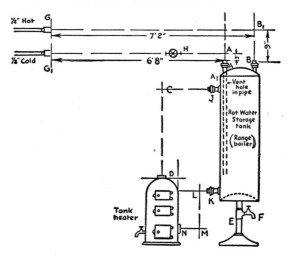

FIG. 4.81.   Diagram of hot water heating system.

ment is found to be 6' 8", and it is marked off on the assembled piece, from the center of the tee, adding $\frac{1}{2}$" for threading into the coupling G_1. The pipe is cut at this point and threaded.

The hot and cold water pipes are now installed and are supported by two hangers near the tank. Measurements are then taken from A to A_1, and from B to B_1. It is now merely necessary to make face-to-face measurements at this point and then to add the necessary amount for threading into the fittings.

Three-quarter inch pipe is used for the part of the system, which connects the heater and tank, in order to obtain good circulation of water from the heater through the tank. A short nipple is first screwed into the tank at the opening near the bottom. A $\frac{3}{4}$" union, K, is screwed on to the nipple, and a $\frac{3}{4}$" street elbow is screwed into the other end of the union.

The measurement is now taken from L to M, which is found to be $12\frac{3}{4}''$. From Table 2, find that the distance from the center of the fitting to the end of the pipe, for a $\frac{3}{4}''$ street elbow, is $1\frac{3}{16}''$. Therefore, subtract twice $1\frac{3}{16}''$, which is $1\frac{5}{8}''$, from the center line measurements, which gives $11\frac{1}{8}''$. This piece of pipe is cut, threaded, and made up with the elbow, and measurement M to N is taken. (If the heater can be moved slightly from its position, it will be best to use a standard nipple for this piece.) After the piece is obtained, the pipes and fittings are disassembled from the union and are made up from the heater end. Finally, the heater is connected to the tank by use of the union. In a similar way, measurements J to C, and C to D, are taken, and the pipe is cut, threaded, and made up by the use of a $\frac{3}{4}''$ union at J.

If measurements are taken carefully, the result will be a neat-looking job, with pipes running truly vertical and horizontal. Brass pipes and fittings should be used for the connection between the heater and the tank. It is preferable to have the whole system made of brass pipe and to use a storage tank that is also made of brass or copper.

Cutting and Assembling Copper Tubes with Solder Fittings. A tube cutter should be used for cutting the tube to length. This may be done by holding the tube and cutter by hand. Special vises which hold the tube and guide the blade of a back saw are also convenient. A piece of channel iron or a wooden frame, slightly larger than the tube, will serve as a guide if a kerf is cut in the channel at right angles to its sides and bottom surface. If the copper tube is cut with a hacksaw, a 32-tooth blade is the type to use. Make certain that the tube ends are cut square.

The burr on the cut end is now removed with the reamer, which is usually on the end of the tube cutter. A file may be used instead of the reamer. The burr on the outside of the tube is removed with a file. If the end of the tube is distorted, due to handling, a sizing tool is used to restore it to its original size and shape.

Prior to soldering, the surfaces of the parts to be joined should be thoroughly cleaned. This operation can be done conveniently as follows: Clean the end and the outside surface of the tube for a distance slightly greater than the depth of the joint, and clean the inside of the fitting up to the shoulder, with No. 00 steel wool or fine emery cloth (No. 0). Be sure to rub the metal until it is bright. All oxide or other discoloration must be removed. The success of all soldering depends greatly on careful preparation and thorough cleaning.

The next step in the work is to apply the flux, preferably a noncorrosive

OPERATIONS IN JOINING COPPER TUBES

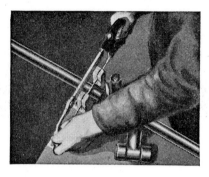

Fig. 4.82.   Cutting copper tube with a hacksaw.

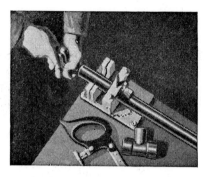

Fig. 4.83.   Reaming a copper tube.

Fig. 4.84.   Cleaning fitting with steel wool.

Fig. 4.85.   Spreading flux on tube and fitting.

Fig 4.86.   Revolving fitting to help spread flux.

Fig. 4.87.   Applying heat to the fitting and testing with solder.

OPERATIONS IN JOINING COPPER TUBES

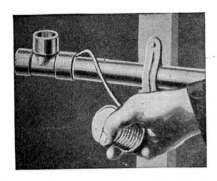

FIG. 4.88. Feeding solder at the edge of fitting.

FIG. 4.89. Wrapped joints to keep solder from melting.

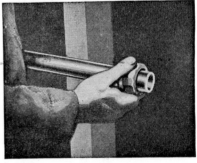

FIG. 4.90. Using an air-acetylene type torch close to wood.

FIG. 4.91. Placing sleeve-nut on section of tube before flaring.

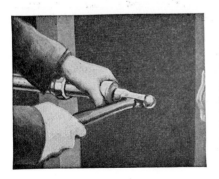

FIG. 4.92. Using the flanging tool.

FIG. 4.93. Drawing the sleeve-nut tight with a monkey wrench.

soldering paste, to the cleaned surfaces of the tube and fitting. Spread the flux in a thin, even coat with a brush, or with clean fingers.

Slip the fitting over the tube as far as it will go and give it a few turns to even up the flux coating on the surfaces to be soldered.

Heat the tube and fitting with a gasoline blow torch or air-acetylene torch, until the flux begins to boil. Immediately touch the edge of the fitting with the wire solder, which will flow and fill the joint almost immediately if the fitting and tube are hot enough. If not, heat a little more. Too much heat will spoil the joint. Be sure enough solder is in the joint before it cools. Wipe off any excess solder with a rag. The joint should show a smooth ring of solder on the tube at the edge of the fitting. Rubbing the finished job, when cool enough, with No. 00 steel wool will produce a neat workmanlike job.

Wrap all completed joints with a wet rag when making other joints on the same fitting, to prevent the solder in the completed joints from melting. Remember that copper is a good conductor of heat.

Wood or other inflammable surfaces should be protected from the flame of the torch by the use of asbestos sheet. On account of its highly concentrated heat, the air-acetylene torch permits work to be done closer to wood than is possible with the gasoline blow torch.

Some fittings are made with a feed hole at each branch. The same soldering procedure is used, except that the solder is fed to the hole instead of to the edge of the fitting. The same smooth ring of solder should appear at the edge of the fitting. Care should be taken to see that the hole remains full of solder at the completion of the joint.

When soldering the large fittings, 2½″ and up, great care should be taken to heat the complete circumference of the fitting.

Joining Copper Tubes with Flared Tube Fittings. Cut and ream the copper tube, as when preparing for a solder joint. Slip the sleeve nut section of the flared copper tube fitting over the copper tube.

Place a few drops of oil on a flanging tool of the correct size and carefully center it in the end of the tube. Strike it squarely in the center with a hammer until the tube is flared to the outside diameter of the flanging tool. To insure a perfect fit, it is important that the flanging tool be kept centered in the end of the copper tube.

The male section of the flared copper tube fitting is now inserted in the sleeve nut and drawn up tight with a monkey wrench. It is sometimes advisable to use two wrenches to make up flared fittings. One is used as described while the other is placed on the body of the fitting to prevent it from turning, in case extra pressure must be used to make the joint tight.

Prevent chips of copper and filings from getting inside the tubing by holding the tube downward, so that dirt will not enter. Refrigeration mechanics pinch the tubing together just beyond the cut, to prevent the entry of foreign matter into tubing which is not to be used immediately.

FIG. 4.94. Yarning.

Connecting Cast-Iron Pipe. Always test cast-iron pipe before starting to make up a line of pipe. Strike the bell and spigot ends of each piece lightly with a hammer. A clear ring indicates a sound pipe. The bell and spigot must be clean and dry before joining.

When joining a vertical line of soil pipe, secure the lower section, bell end up. Then insert the spigot end of the next higher section into the bell to its full depth and secure the upper pipe in a vertical position. The joint is now ready to be filled with oakum or to be "yarned," which is the trade term for this operation.

Twist about 2' of oakum into a tight rope by holding one end in the hand and rolling the loose strands against the thigh, until the length is so thick that it can just be pressed into the open joint by hand. Hold one end and wind the rope of oakum once around the pipe, just above the hub. With the yarning iron in the other hand, drive the oakum down to the bottom of the joint space. Continue wrapping and driving by hand until the joint is filled to within ½″ of the rim of the hub. Using a hammer, and a wide and thick iron, drive the oakum down as tightly as possible, until there is a uniform surface all around about an inch from the top. No loose fibers or strands should be left protruding to cause leaks. They may be burned off easily with a blow-torch if necessary.

FIG. 4.95.   Pouring a vertical joint in cast-iron pipe.

Light the gasoline fire pot and melt a sufficient amount of lead to be poured in the joint. Lay the ladle over the fire pot, so that it will heat before it is dipped into the molten lead, as an explosion may result from dipping a cold ladle in the molten lead. When the lead has melted, skim off the slag, or dross, with the ladle, then dip out a ladleful, and pour the hot lead into the joint. Move the ladle all around the joint, quickly at first, and continue to pour until the lead stands about ⅛″ above the hub. The molten lead should not be allowed to solidify before the entire joint is poured.

The joint and the hub must cool before the caulking is begun. While waiting for the joint to cool, the next lengths of pipe may be yarned and poured.

The next and last step is very important and must be done carefully. The caulking operation is intended to pack the soft lead firmly against the sides of the pipe inside the joint. It is not intended merely to drive the lead ring down into the space between spigot and hub. Lead shrinks slightly as it cools; therefore, it is necessary to use the caulking tools to pack the joint and to take up this slight shrinkage.

Using a light hammer and the inside caulking iron, start at the most inaccessible part of the joint and pack the lead down firmly all around the

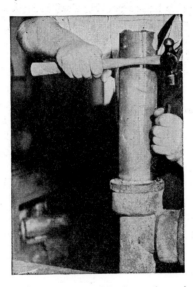

FIG. 4.96.   Caulking a joint in cast-iron pipe.

spigot end.   The hammer strokes must be firm taps, not full hammer blows, or the lead will be jarred loose.   This operation is intended to pack the lead more tightly against the pipe surface inside the hub.   After the first edge has been set down, take the *outside* caulking iron and repeat the process around the joint next to the hub, using the same hammer and tapping strokes.   As a final operation, the joint may be finished by using a wide and thick finishing tool on the flat surface of the lead, to give a final packing to the joint.   This must be done very carefully, however, because the lead that is tightly compressed against the iron surfaces down in the joint must not be jarred loose, or leaks will develop.

A horizontal run of pipe is prepared for jointing by laying each pipe on blocks or bricks, so that there is plenty of room to work all around each hub. If the pipes are first laid in a trench, and then caulked in that position, a small hole should be scooped out under each hub, to permit ample working space.

Yarn each joint, as explained previously, and line up the run of pipe with a piece of string before the final yarning is completed. The last piece of pipe should be braced against something solid, to prevent end play in the line as each joint is caulked. Check again with a string along the top and one side of the pipe line before pouring the hot lead. Do not shift joints to make them line up by hammering them into line. Use a piece of wood or a bar to shift the hubs in to the correct alignment. Always remember — a cracked hub is a ruined hub!

An asbestos joint-runner is used when working on a horizontal run of pipe. It is wrapped around the pipe just above a hub, as tightly as possible, and clipped firmly with the clamp provided for that purpose. The clip is always placed on the top of the pipe, thus forming a convenient funnel where the runner is held together. Tap the asbestos runner down against the top of the hub, so that there is no place for the hot lead to run out of the joint when it is poured.

Pour the joint in a single operation, standing well back of the ladle. Use a ladle that is large enough to fill the joint to overflowing with one pouring. If possible, several joints may be yarned and then poured one after

FIG. 4.97.   Section of a joint
in cast-iron soil pipe.

another, so that the first one may be cooling as the others are being poured. This saves time. Allow all the joints and hubs to cool before beginning the final caulking with irons. Remove the joint runner as soon as the lead has solidified and use it on the next joint.

There will always be a ring of excess lead showing above the hub on a well formed rough joint. This must be set down firmly at four points around the hub, using the inside caulking iron and striking firm hammer blows. Then cut off the surplus lead flush with the top of the hub, using a sharp cold chisel. If the joint is knocked out of the hub, or loosened by the hammer blows, the joint must be melted out and run in again.

The final caulking, using both the inside and outside caulking irons, is shown in Fig. 4.96. Use the inside iron first, going all around the joint where it touches the spigot end of the pipe. Each stroke must overlap the previous stroke slightly. Keep the point of the iron pressed against the wall of the pipe as each stroke is driven home. When the inner crack has been set down, the same operation is repeated all around the outer edge of the joint where it touches the hub. Use the outside caulking tool for this work and keep the point pressed against the inside edge of the bell as the joint is worked all around.

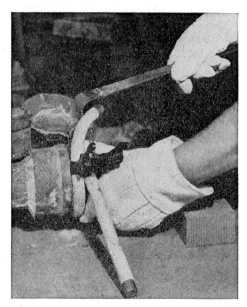

FIG. 4.98. Pouring a joint in a horizontal run of iron pipe.

Melting Out Joints in a Run of Horizontal Cast-Iron Soil Pipe. Joints in cast-iron pipe usually are melted out with a gasoline torch. The torch flame is applied to the bottom of the hub near the end, until the lead has melted and run out. The torch is then moved progressively up and around the joint. A sheet of black iron should be placed under the hub, if possible, to catch the lead.

Melting Lead for Use in Caulking. Only good, clean soft lead will produce tight joints. It is a temptation to use scrap lead because it may be cheap, but excessive drossing and caulking difficulties will cancel any savings in cost. The Lead Industries Association has set a standard of purity for caulking lead, and all bars that meet this specification are stamped with a seal of approval.   The melting pot is a source of trouble if it is not kept clean.   All dross, lead oxide, and crusts of dirt must be removed from time to time and the inside of the pot cleaned with a wire brush.   Lead oxide forms rapidly if the lead is overheated.   The furnace must therefore be regulated so that the lead is melted, but not cooked to oxidation.

Start the furnace according to the manufacturer's recommendations. Stand a small piece of pure lead on end in the pot so that it will melt rapidly. Add more pieces as the first chunks melt, but always *dry each piece thoroughly* before adding it to the molten lead.   Place the ladle on the edge of the pot to dry and warm it before use.

Do not stir molten lead, because stirring hastens excessive oxidation. To dip out a ladleful of hot lead it is only necessary to push back the scum of dross that will always form on top and dip into the clean lead thus exposed.   Use the *back* of the ladle to expose enough lead, and then just tip the front lip down far enough to fill the bowl.   Keep the hand well away from the bowl all the time.   Return any left-over lead to the pot, without splashing, as soon as possible.

Chapter 4

~~~~~~

HOUSE PLUMBING JOBS

Draining the Plumbing System when Closing the House for the Winter . . . Repairing Faucet and Valve Leaks . . . Replacing a Bad Section of Pipe with New Pipe and Fittings . . . Maintenance of the Toilet Tanks . . . Cleaning a Trap . . . Removing and Replacing a Toilet Bowl . . . Thawing of Frozen Pipes . . . Installing a Basin, a Small Plumbing Fixture . . . Building a Dry Well or a Small Cesspool . . . Maintenance of the Radiator . . . Maintenance of the Heating Unit

Draining the Plumbing System when Closing the House for the Winter. Job No. 1. It is necessary to shut off the water, and drain the plumbing system, before closing the house for the winter. A considerable amount of damage can result from bursting water pipes, not only to the plumbing fixtures and fittings, but also to the house itself, during the period of thawing. A portion of the house may be flooded if the main valves are not closed. Therefore, it is of the utmost importance that the home owner take an unusual amount of care in seeing that all the water is drained from the pipes and fittings, before the house is left to stand idle during the winter.

In order to complete the draining of the plumbing system, an orderly method must be planned. As there are differences in all plumbing systems, many of the problems that the home owner may face cannot be anticipated. However, there are a few general rules that may be followed, which will help in carrying out this job in an orderly manner.

Draining the Hot and Cold Water Supply Pipes. The first step in draining the water supply pipes is to close the shut-off at the curb, if the water supply comes from a water main in the street. This is done by removing the cover from the curb shut-off housing and turning the extension rod one quarter of a turn with a wrench. After the curb shut-off is closed, the pressure should be checked in the house, to make sure that this valve is closed entirely. The shut-off valve, which is just inside the foundation of the house, may be a gate valve, a globe valve, or a ground-key valve. The valve is usually provided with a drain which, when open, will drain the water that may be left standing in the pipe near the valve.

By means of a hose connected to the drain faucet under the hot water tank, drain the water from this tank.   If the position of the hot water tank is such that the water will not run from the hose to a convenient drain in the cellar, it must be drained into a pail.   In order to allow the water to run out of the tank and pipes, all hot water faucets must be opened in the fixtures, to permit air to enter the pipe and tank and replace the water.

The cold water pipe may be drained by disconnecting the pipe nearest the meter, which is done by opening a union in the pipe.   A sufficient number of containers must be provided, in order that the water may not drain onto the cellar floor.   The flow of the water from the pipe may be controlled by having a second person open the cold water faucet in a fixture, closing the faucet when the container is full.   When the tank and pipes are drained, open all the valves and faucets in the system.

The system should be carefully examined to see that there is no out-of-the-way section in which the water may be pocketed, due to the lack of proper pitch in the pipe.   Examine the horizontal pipes in the cellar especially and, if this condition is found to exist, disconnect the pipe and drain it from the nearest union.

Some equipment, such as the hot water heating stove near the hot water tank, may require special attention, if the pipe is arranged so that it will not drain readily.   If this is the case, disconnect the equipment and drain the water from it.   It is reasonably certain that there is no water left in a section of pipe if air will pass through the pipe by blowing in a faucet or union.   The sill cocks should be opened, and the valves that control the flow of water to the sill cocks should also be opened and drained.

Some water meters are provided with a drain at the bottom; however, if this is not the case, the meter should be disconnected and drained.   Water meters are usually connected to the water line and sealed by the water company, to prevent the home owner from tampering with them.   Do not break this seal without permission.   In some localities the water company will send a man to remove the meter when the house is to be left vacant.   If there is any question as to whether or not water is left in the meter, it is a good plan to wrap the meter with some insulating material to help keep it from freezing.

Draining Traps.   After the supply pipes have been thoroughly drained, all the fixtures must be carefully examined to see that there is no water left standing in the pipes.

The toilet tank must be drained.   Empty the toilet tank by flushing, and then sponge the bottom of the tank to make sure it is thoroughly dry.   The trap in the toilet bowl may be filled with kerosene to replace the water.

This method is preferred to removing the water only, because if the trap is emptied and left without any liquid seal, sewer gas may accumulate in the house.

Each fixture in the house that is connected to the drainage system is provided with a trap. The basin trap in the bathroom should be either drained or filled with a substantial amount of kerosene. A drain plug is usually provided at the bottom of the trap for the purpose of draining. This may be unscrewed with a pair of pliers, collecting the water in a pail or container. The bathtub trap is usually concealed in the floor and may be emptied of water by filling it with kerosene. In some cases, access to the bathtub trap is provided in the bathroom floor by a plug, which may be removed for draining. Some tub-trap drain plugs are located on the ceiling of the room directly under the bathroom. The traps in the laundry tubs and kitchen sink should also be drained, or filled with kerosene.

An anti-freeze solution that does not evaporate may be used in place of kerosene to fill the traps. These solutions are preferable, because they will mix with whatever water may be left in the trap. Alcohol should not be used for this purpose, because it will evaporate, leaving a considerable amount of water in the trap.

Draining the Heating System. The steam or hot water heating systems must be thoroughly drained before closing the house for the winter. The furnace is provided with a drain cock onto which a hose may be connected. If the furnace is in such a location that a hose cannot be used to drain the water from the furnace because of its low level, it must be drained into containers and carried outside. All the valves in the heating system should be opened, when draining, to make sure that all the water is drained from the radiators. Even a small amount of water left in the radiator may cause considerable damage. To be sure that there is no water left in the radiator after the furnace is drained, disconnect the radiator at the shut-off valve, and drain the water that remains at the bottom of the radiator into a small container.

Miscellaneous. The traps in the drainage system in the cellar, water storage tanks, expansion tanks in the attic, and water pumps, must all be considered before closing the house for the winter. This equipment must be examined to see that all the water has been removed.

All the valves in the plumbing system should be left open and, if a drain plug is provided on the valve, the water should be drained through this plug. Water left standing in a valve may become frozen. Valves that are placed in a horizontal run of pipe in the cellar should be disassembled by unscrewing the bonnet nut. Be sure to place any part that is removed from the system, for drainage, in a conspicuous place, so that it may be easily found when the water system is turned on again. A list of the openings made in the water supply and drainage systems should be kept, so that a check can be made when the water is to be turned on.

Turning On the Water in the House after the Water Has Been Drained for Cold Weather. If a list has been kept of all the openings that were made in the plumbing system when the water was shut off, the job of turning on the water will be simplified, and there will be less chance of having water, from a forgotten opening, run onto valuable house furnishings.

1. Be sure that the drain plug in the trap of each fixture has been replaced.

2. Connect the meter, if it has been removed.

3. Connect all sections of pipe that have been disconnected for draining.

4. Replace the bonnets that have been unscrewed from the valves on the horizontal pipes in the cellar.

5. Close the section of pipe nearest the main shut-off valve, by shutting off all branch control valves in the cellar.

6. Close the main shut-off valve near the foundation and turn on the water at the curb.

7. Cautiously open the main shut-off valve, noticing whether any leak appears in the main section of pipe which has been closed. If no leak appears, and there is no audible indication of water running through the pipes, leave this valve open. If a leak appears in this section, the water must be shut off and the leak repaired.

8. Each branch section should be turned on cautiously, to make sure that there is no leak due to an opening in the system that has not been closed, or due to freezing of the pipes or fittings.

Too much stress cannot be placed upon the care that should be taken in turning on the water, as considerable damage may result from too much haste. It is a good plan to have some help in doing this job, in order to observe sections of the piping that cannot be seen by the individual controlling the valve.

Repairing Faucet and Valve Leaks. Job No. 2. Faucet and valve leaks are usually due to one or the other of two faults. The leak may be caused by insufficient packing around the valve stem, or it may be caused by improper seating of the washer on the valve seat. To stop the dripping of water around the valve stem, it may be merely necessary to tighten the packing nut at the valve stem. However, in some cases where this does not stop the water from dripping, the packing in the packing nut must be replaced.

Replacing the Packing in a Valve or Faucet.

1. If the valve is a globe valve, shut off the valve, but, if it is a gate valve, it is usually necessary to turn off the water in the line before the valve stem is packed.

2. Remove the packing nut and old packing.

3. Wind a sufficient amount of wicking around the valve stem under the nut, in the same direction that you turn the nut when tightening.

FIG. 4.99.   Packing a valve stem with wicking.

4. Replace the packing nut, tightening it just enough to permit the valve stem to operate without leakage.

5. Radiators are controlled by globe or angle valves and may be maintained in this manner.   It is important to have no leakage in a stem heating system, in order to maintain a partial vacuum in the system, which increases heating efficiency.   Specially prepared packing may be used instead of wicking.

Replacing a Washer in a Compression Faucet.   If the faucet continues to drip after it is turned off, the probability is that it needs a new washer.   An assortment of composition disk washers and brass screws may be obtained for this purpose in a hardware store.

1. Shut off the water at the nearest point to the leaking faucet and open the faucet in order to let the water drain.

2. Remove the cap nut with a monkey wrench, taking care not to scratch the plating.

3. Unscrew the valve stem from the body.

4. Remove the old washer by unscrewing the brass screw in the center of the washer.

5. Select, from your assortment, the proper size of washer to fit the faucet and replace the brass screw if the old screw is badly corroded.   Replace the

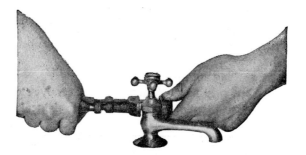

FIG. 4.100. Removing the cap nut.

FIG. 4.101. Removing the valve stem.

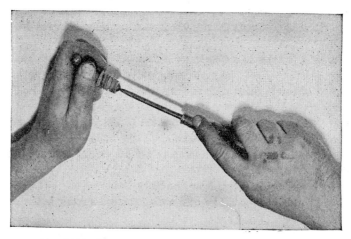

FIG. 4.102. Unscrewing screw holding washer in valve stem.

valve stem in the body of the faucet and the cap nut, using enough pressure when tightening the cap nut to prevent water from leaking through the packing around the stem.

Replacing a Fuller Ball. If the faucet is of the Fuller-ball type, a leak may be caused by improper seating of the ball. Remove the faucet and examine the parts for undue wear. If either the valve rod or eccentric on the spindle guide is worn badly, the parts should be replaced.

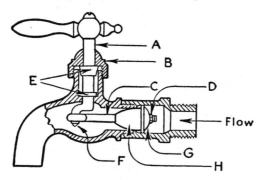

FIG. 4.103.   Fuller-ball faucet.

An adjusting screw is provided to adjust the Fuller ball so that it will seat itself in the valve seat. This may be the only attention that is needed, providing the ball is not worn badly. If the ball needs replacement, loosen the adjustment screw, remove the cap and replace the ball. Set the adjusting screw so that the ball seats itself when the handle is in the off position, and replace the faucet.

Dressing the Worn Seat on a Compression Type Faucet. If the washer on a faucet is not replaced when a leak appears, continual use may cause damage to the seat of the faucet. If the seat has been nicked or roughened by a badly worn washer, replacement of the washer may not stop the leak. If such a condition exists, either the faucet must be replaced, or the seat must be dressed with a special seat-dressing tool. This tool acts as a rotary file, which machines the seat in such a manner that the washer will fit properly when the valve is closed. Seat dressers are made in various designs and, therefore, must be used according to the directions provided with the tool. Care must be taken after using the dresser to see that all filings are flushed from the faucet before the water is used.

Replacing a Faulty Section of Pipe with New Pipe and Fittings. Job No. 3. A leak may appear in a section of pipe which has been damaged by corrosion or freezing. If the pipes are badly corroded it is best to remove and examine the pipe and fittings to see how far the condition has gone. In the case of a system using iron pipe, a leak caused by corrosion may be an indication that the whole water supply system is deterioriating, and may require replacement of the entire system of pipes. However, if the condition is local, replacement of a short length of pipe or fitting may be all that is necessary. Where iron pipe is used around the hot water tank, corrosion occurs rapidly and requires replacement periodically. If a major job is anticipated, it is well to consider the possibility of changing from iron pipe to brass or to copper tubing. The savings in later years will offset the initial cost of materials and labor.

Measurements may be taken directly from the pipe line that is to be replaced, if there is to be no change in the position of the pipe.

Procedure:

1. Shut off the water in the pipe that is to be repaired.

2. Locate the union nearest to the section that needs to be repaired and disconnect the pipe at the union. Drain the pipe, if possible, by opening a drain cock at a low point in the system. *Caution:* Be sure to provide a container to drain whatever water may be left in the pipe. It is wise to open the faucet at a higher level so that air may enter the pipe, and the pipe may be fully drained.

3. Disconnect whatever pipe is necessary to remove the pieces that are to be replaced. If no union can be found near the piece that is to be replaced, it may be necessary to cut the pipe and to insert a union somewhere in this section when connecting the pipe after replacement. It is best to use a hack saw for cutting this pipe.

4. Measure the old pieces of pipe and cut the new pipe of the same diameter and to the same length.

5. Ream and thread each of these pieces.

6. Make up the pipe, starting with the last piece that was removed. (Cover the male thread with pipe joint compound.)

7. Connect the new section of pipe with the line by using a union. If the old union is of the gasket type, a new fiber gasket must be used in its place to ensure a tight joint.

Pipe joint compound should not be used in connecting the union, except on the parts of the pipe that screw directly into the union. It is advisable to replace gasket-type unions with ground-seat unions, if the union is apt to be disconnected at short intervals.

Maintenance of the Toilet Tanks. Job No. 4. At least once a year, the toilet tank mechanism should be checked and adjusted. The amount of water in the tank when it is full should be just enough to flush the bowl. Too much water in the tank is wasteful because extra water has no function in the flushing and, therefore, merely runs down the drain. A considerable saving can be made on the water bill by preventing such a condition. Some tank mechanisms are provided with an adjustment screw which controls the level of the float when it is at the "off" position. Other mechanisms may be adjusted by bending the float rod slightly, in order that the valve may be shut off when sufficient water is in the tank.

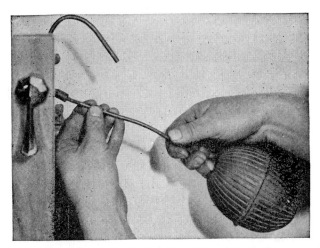

FIG. 4.104. Adjusting the float valve rod by bending.

If the water in the tank shows a slight movement when the float is in the "off" position, there may be a leak at the float valve. If the float valve leaks it may be removed and a new washer inserted.

Removal of the Float Valve.

1. Shut off the water at the nearest valve to the flush tank.
2. Flush away the water in the tank.
3. Sponge out the remaining water at the bottom of the tank.
4. Unscrew the float and float rod.
5. Disconnect the supply pipe at the union under the tank.
6. Remove the nut, under the tank, that holds the float valve in place.
7. Take the float valve apart and replace the washer.

8. Reassemble the valve and float.

9. Connect the supply pipe.

10. Turn on the water and check the operation of the valve.

In sections of the country where water is unusually corrosive, the entire float valve corrodes rapidly and, therefore, requires replacement.

Quite often a leak develops at the flush valve. Since the flush valve controls the flow of water from the tank into the bowl, a leak of this kind is indi-

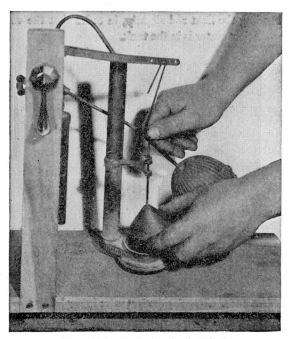

Fig. 4.105. Replacing the flush ball.

cated by a movement of water in the bowl, however slight, after the tank is filled. The leak may generally be corrected by removing and replacing the rubber flush ball which is screwed to a brass rod. Sometimes, however, the leak is caused by shifting of the flush-ball rod guide. The guide should center the flush ball directly over the flush valve seat. Be sure the flush ball is not held up by the rod connected to the trip lever. The flush ball rod should extend through the loop in the lever rod about 1″ to avoid this condition.

The entire flush valve seat and overflow assembly may be replaced, if parts are corroded badly.

Replacing the Flush Valve Seat and Overflow Assembly.

1. Turn off the water at the nearest valve which controls the water entering the tank.

2. Flush the tank and sponge out the remaining water at the bottom of the tank.

3. Unscrew the slip-joint nut which holds the plated brass elbow tube in place.

4. If necessary, unscrew the slip-joint nut connecting the elbow to the bowl and remove the elbow.

5. Unscrew the nut which holds the flush valve assembly at the bottom of the tank.

6. Remove the old assembly and replace it with the new.

7. Tighten the nut on the bottom of the tank which secures the assembly to the tank.

8. Replace the elbow and tighten the slip-joint nuts.

9. If a leak appears at the joint, either new rubber packing may be obtained or the nut may be packed by using wicking in the same manner as when packing a valve stem.

Care must be taken not to use too much force when tightening holding nuts, when working on fixtures made of vitreous china. A special soft rubber gasket is provided for connections with these fixtures. If this gasket is in good condition, the connection will be water tight with a minimum amount of pressure. The trip lever assembly may also be purchased as a unit and replaced when parts are badly corroded or worn.

Cleaning a Trap. Job No. 5. *Cleaning a Trap by Draining the Trap from the Clean-out Plug.* Poor drainage from fixtures may be caused by sediment or solid material accumulating in the trap. This material may be removed by draining and cleaning the trap. Secure a container large enough to hold the amount of water in the trap and unscrew the drain plug with a pair of pliers. Twist together two pieces of soft iron wire, leaving the ends hooked, as shown in Fig. 4.106. Insert the wire into the opening at the bottom of the trap and "snake" it through the trap, in order to remove the lint and hair that may have accumulated. Flush the trap with clean water and replace the drain plug. Most traps are constructed so that they may be drained and cleaned from a drain plug at the lowest part of the trap; however, some traps are designed without drain plugs. If necessary, the latter may be cleaned by disconnecting at the joint and using the wire in the same manner as was described above.

Using a Drain Cleaner. Quite often it is satisfactory to clean a drain by using a chemical, rather than a mechanical, means of cleaning. There are many drain cleaners on the market which may be used without injury to the drainage system. Use these cleaners, however, according to the directions on the label, taking care not to spill them on the floor or on any finished sur-

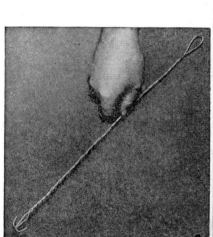 

FIG. 4.106. Clean-out wire for sink trap. FIG. 4.107. Draining and cleaning a sink trap.

face. Most of the cleaners contain lye, which will attack linoleum or paint and, if used carelessly, may cause much damage.

After the chemical cleaner has been standing in the drain for 10 or 15 minutes, the drain may be "forced" by using the "plumber's friend" which is a rubber suction cup with a handle for pumping, or plunging, the sediment in the clogged drain pipe. Fill the fixture with water and then drain it, using the "plumber's friend" to force the clean water through the drain pipe.

Using a Clean-out Auger to Remove Obstacles from the Toilet Bowl. Drain cleaners are of very little use in cleaning large drains, such as the toilet bowl. If the toilet bowl trap becomes stopped, it is usually necessary to remove the obstruction by mechanical means, for example, with a "plumber's friend."

However, if this method does not clear the trap, other methods must be adopted.

The clean-out auger may be used if the obstruction cannot be forced through the trap by plunging. Insert the end of the flexible cable in the trap, forcing it through as far as possible by turning the crank handle on the clean-out auger. When the auger has reached the obstruction, the

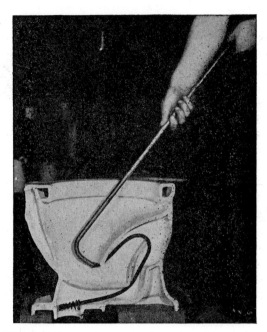

Fig. 4.108. Toilet bowl cut away showing action of the clean-out auger.

obstruction may have become entangled on the auger and, if so, may be removed by drawing the auger from the bowl. Keep turning the auger in the same direction as you remove it.

Sometimes a piece of glass or metal becomes lodged in the trap in such a position that it is impossible to remove it by either of the former methods. In this case the toilet bowl must be removed and the obstruction forced out from the other end of the trap. The procedure for removing the toilet bowl will be outlined in Job No. 6.

Cleaning a Length of Drain Pipe. If, after the trap has been cleaned thoroughly, the water in a sink, tub, or basin continues to run out slowly, the trouble may be that the length of drain pipe connecting the trap with a vertical stack is clogged. In some cases where this drain is accessible, such as the fixtures on the first floor of a dwelling, the drain pipe may be examined from the cellar. Many sluggish drains are caused by sediment accumulating in a horizontal drain pipe which has been installed without the proper pitch. If this is the case, the horizontal run of pipe may be cleaned by opening the drain plug at the end of the pipe and loosening the sediment with either a piece of wire or a clean-out auger. Care must be taken when removing a clean-out plug in the drainage system to be sure that the water that may be standing in the drain flows into a container large enough to take care of it. In some cases, where there is no provision for cleaning by removing a clean-out plug, a small hole may be drilled in a pipe or fitting for insertion of the clean-out wire. This hole should be the size of a standard pipe "tap drill" so that it may readily be tapped, using a pipe tap. After the pipe is cleaned, the hole may be closed by the use of a standard pipe plug of the proper size.

Removing and Replacing a Toilet Bowl. Job No. 6. In renovating a bathroom, it is necessary quite often to remove fixtures from the floor in order to replace the floor covering. When laying new linoleum on a bathroom floor, it is more satisfactory to remove fixtures than to cut the linoleum and leave a joint from the fixture to the wall. If this job is anticipated it must be certain that the fixtures are handled carefully, for the expense of replacing broken fixtures will not justify tackling the job.

The toilet bowl is usually connected to the toilet tank by a plated elbow which may be removed by unscrewing a packing nut at the tank and at the bowl. Care must be taken to turn the nut in the proper direction and not to force it, as a crack may be produced on the bowl. In some cases, in order to remove the bowl, it is necessary also to remove the tank from the wall. If this is the case, the water supply should first be shut off from the tank, and then the tank is emptied by flushing. The tank is disconnected from the water supply by unscrewing the union nut underneath the tank. The tank is fastened to the wall by wood or lag screws, which are then removed.

Removing the Toilet Bowl. Before removing the toilet bowl, the water in the trap should be emptied by bailing or pumping. The bowl may now be removed by unscrewing the hold-down nuts at the base. In some cases these hold-down nuts are covered with porcelain caps which are fitted over the nut with putty to conceal the nut. This cap may be removed by tapping lightly with a mallet. The toilet bowl may be eased away from the floor now by jarring it slightly with the hand. Old putty may be removed from the bottom of the toilet bowl with a putty knife.

Replacing the Toilet Bowl. Before replacing the toilet bowl, be sure the floor under the bowl has been cleaned and is dry. Clean all the old putty from the closet flange and replace badly worn or corroded hold-down bolts. If a gasket is used for the connection, it should be inspected and replaced if found to be defective. Approximately 3 lbs. of putty will be required to replace the joint between the toilet bowl and the floor. The putty is generously spread on the bottom of the toilet bowl; the toilet bowl is placed in position; and the "hold-down" nuts are tightened until the bowl sets level on the floor. The excess putty is cut away from the joint with a putty knife. If the tank has been removed, replace the tank and the plated elbow. Note the condition of the rubber packing washers in the elbow nuts and replace them if they are badly worn. Connect the supply pipe to the bottom of the supply tank and turn on the water.

Thawing Out Frozen Pipes. Job No. 7. When thawing a frozen pipe, preparations should be made for turning off the water quickly, at the main valve, in case a leak develops. Examine the pipes for cracks before thawing and remove and replace pipes and fittings that are cracked. (See Job No. 3.) If the pipe does not seem to be cracked, leave the main valve turned on and open the faucets in the fixtures that are affected by the frozen pipe. Heat may then be applied to the pipe nearest the fixture. Always work toward the main shut-off valve, so that the melting ice can thus run out of the faucet.

A blow torch may be used in thawing pipes; however, care should be taken to see that any wood that may be exposed to the flame is protected by a piece of asbestos board. A convenient way to heat some accessible pipes is by pouring boiling water over them. Pipes that are continually exposed to freezing temperatures should be insulated. A pipe may be enclosed in a box, which may then be filled with an insulating material, or standard air-cell asbestos pipe covering may be used. The application of this type of insulation is explained on page 35.

Installing a Basin or Small Plumbing Fixture. Job No. 8. Before attempting a job of this type, visit the local authorities to ascertain whether or not existing restrictions forbid the home owner from making connections to the drainage system. However, in some small communities there are no restrictions and, therefore, it is permissible for one to do work of this kind.

If the basin or fixture is to be placed in a room that is being renovated, the supply, drainage, and vent pipes can be installed in the wall conveniently. Manufacturers usually supply "roughing-in" dimensions with new fixtures. If these dimensions are available, they may be used to locate the pipes in the wall. If no "roughing-in" dimensions are available, measurements may be taken from the fixture. In cases where the fixture is to be hung on the finished wall, the pipes must necessarily be exposed. This requires measuring for, and drilling holes in, the floor to permit the supply and waste pipes to be connected to the fixture.

Basins are usually placed 30″ from the floor level. It is customary for the hot water faucet to be on the left and the cold water on the right. Begin measuring for the supply pipe from the nearest branch available. Plan to connect into this branch with a tee. If the pipe in this branch is ¾″, a reducing tee may be used (¾″ × ¾″ × ½″) so that a ½″ pipe may be run to the floor below the fixture. Use a ½″ × ⅜″ elbow at the end of the horizontal run, if the supply pipes are to be exposed. If the supply pipes are to be run through the wall, use a ½″ elbow and ½″ vertical pipe with ½″ × ⅜″ elbow for connection of a ⅜″ plated supply pipe directly under the fixture. Measure and make up each section of pipe, starting at the branch "T," and working to the hole made in the floor for the supply pipe. The hot water branch supply is made up in the same manner. It may be advisable to place a shut-off valve conveniently somewhere in each branch supply line so that work may be done on the line without shutting off the entire water supply.

The drain pipe for the fixture may run outside the house into a small cesspool, or it may be connected to the drainage system in the house. If the house drainage system can be conveniently tapped for the fixture, this may be more advisable. Begin to make up the drain pipe from a few feet outside the foundation wall, if a cesspool is to be used, or from a convenient point in the drainage system, if the house drain is to be tapped. Make sure that in any horizontal run of drain pipe there is sufficient pitch to allow the drain water to run off. At the fixture end of the horizontal run, a sanitary drainage tee should be used, with a plug in one end to provide an opening for cleaning this run of pipe. It is preferable to install the vertical drain in such a manner that it may be vented through the roof of the building. This pipe, therefore, should extend up through the wall, using a sanitary "T" for connecting it with the basin trap, and continuing the 1½″ vertical pipe through to the roof. A sheet metal roof flange is used on the roof joint to prevent roof leaks. Use special galvanized drainage fittings and galvanized pipes for the drainage installation. The accompanying figure shows model drainage systems that are considered good practice. When venting the fixture, it is important to provide an air inlet, as near the trap as possible, so that the flow of water does not cause siphoning of the trap seal. If the trap seal is broken, sewer gas may enter the house and cause an unhealthy condition.

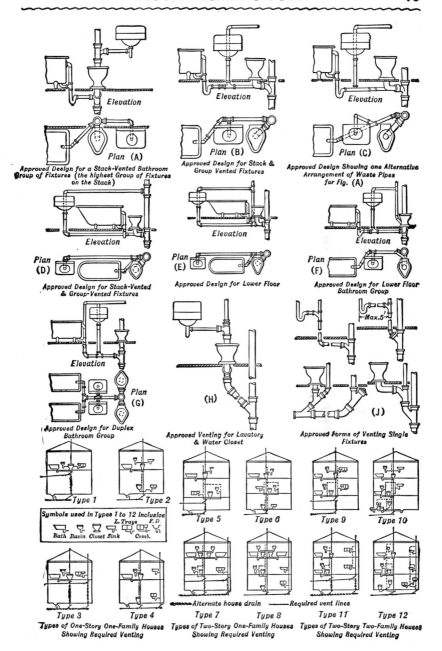

FIG. 4.109. Plumbing installations recommended by "Hoover Report."

After the piping is installed the fixture hanger bracket is fastened to the wall in its proper place. Extra reinforcements may be placed in the wall behind the fixture bracket as a means for fastening the fixture securely. This reinforcement may be made by fitting a 2 × 4 between the studs in the wall. Before the fixture is hung, the faucets may be fastened in place. Place a little white lead or putty under the flange of the faucet, before fastening to the fixture. Fittings such as "P.O." plugs or waste valve assemblies are fastened to the fixture using white lead or putty under the flanges to prevent leakage. The fixture is now hung on the fixture bracket.

Most faucets are provided with a tailpiece threaded for $\frac{1}{4}''$ pipe. Measurements may now be taken from this tailpiece to the reducing elbow in the wall or floor. Use $\frac{3}{8}''$ chrome-plated supply pipe for all exposed piping and plan to connect the $\frac{3}{8}''$ supply pipe to the faucet by using a $\frac{3}{8}'' \times \frac{1}{4}''$ reducing coupling. The pipe is cut and made up carefully, using plated floor or wall flanges to cover the holes made for the pipe. The tailpiece is connected to the faucet by a union nut, which completes the installation of the supply line.

A connection from the sanitary "Y" in the drain pipe in the wall to the fixture is made with a $1\frac{1}{2}''$ nipple of the proper length and a "P" trap. The trap should be brass with heavy plating. The connection between the trap and the drain valve is made with plated brass tubing of the proper size.

An alternate method of connecting the drain is by the use of an "S" trap which will permit connection through the floor rather than through the wall. The "S" trap is easier to install but is not permitted in some localities because of the difficulty in venting such a trap.

Provision should be made for the support of all horizontal pipes. A specially prepared compound may be used to make a water-resistant joint between the fixture and the wall. Care should be taken in measuring and fitting exposed supply pipes, to see that they are installed in a true vertical line and not marred by the careless use of a Stillson wrench.

Building a Dry Well or a Small Cesspool. Job No. 9. Rain water, draining from the roof through the gutter and leader pipes, may be disposed of in several ways. It may run directly onto the ground, it may be discharged into the drainage system, or it may be drained into a small hole in the ground, which is known as a dry well. If the leader from the roof cannot be connected conveniently to the house drainage system, the best method of taking care of this water is by means of the dry well. One type of dry well is constructed by digging a hole about 3' in diameter and 4' deep, about 3' away from the foundation of the house, and by inserting a wooden barrel. The bottom of this barrel may be knocked out, and the barrel filled with stones. The area of the roof, and the number of leaders from the roof, will determine the size of the well. In some localities where drainage is poor, the well must be made deeper on this account.

If the well is to be larger than the "barrel size" well, its walls may be lined with concrete cesspool blocks, which may be obtained from any concrete building block manufacturer. These blocks are inexpensive and may be laid up without the use of mortar. They are curved and their ends are so made that they interlock to form a circular container. Dig the hole with straight sides and make sure the bottom of the hole is level.

Start the wall by laying several blocks on the level bottom to form a circle. This circle should be as large as the size of the hole permits. The next tier of blocks is laid so that the joints are staggered, as in laying up bricks. (See Chapter on Brick Construction.) Measure and estimate the number of tiers required to build the sides of the well to a height that will allow the cover to be slightly below the surface of the ground. A reinforced concrete cover for the well may be made or purchased at the same time as the blocks.

The sides of the well may taper toward the top, in order that a cover smaller than the diameter of the bottom of the well may be used. The taper in the well is obtained by leaving out one block in each successive course. The depth of the well, and the diameter at the bottom, will determine how many such tapered courses are necessary. Quite often it is desirable to take apart and rebuild a section of the well, in order that the last course be ended properly.

Provision is made near the top of the well for entrance of a clay drain pipe, which may be laid in a trench connecting the well with a leader pipe from the roof. This drain pipe may be laid without cementing the joints. The drain pipe must also have a slight amount of pitch. About 1' in 20' is considered sufficient. A flat stone placed over each underground joint will help keep sand or dirt from entering the pipe. The connection between the leader and the clay pipe may be made by using a clay elbow, arranged in such a position that the metal leader pipe will enter the elbow. This joint should be sealed with cement.

The sides of the hole should be filled with clean sand to provide better drainage from the well. The well may be covered with 3 or 4" of top soil.

The same type of well may be used as a small cesspool to take care of waste from the kitchen sink or basin. Such a cesspool should be constructed, if possible, in a location where there is natural drainage. Care should be taken in the selection of the location to make sure that the cesspool is not filled with water draining from the ground surrounding it. Advantage may be taken of a sloping land; however, the cesspool should not be located at the lowest point of the slope. Plan to have the hole deep enough to permit the clay drain pipe to enter the cesspool near the top. Provision must also be made for the proper pitch of the clay drain pipe and for venting the small cesspool.

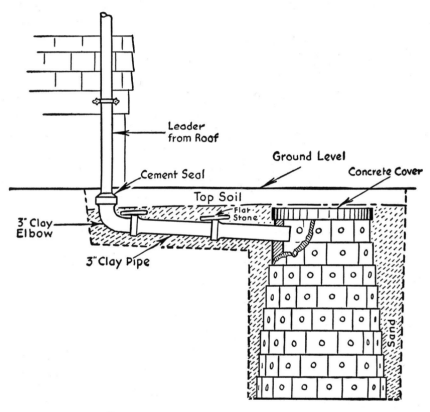

FIG. 4.110.   A dry well for taking care of rain water.

The clay drain pipe joints may be sealed with cement. The joint between the clay pipe and the iron pipe from the fixture should be made a few feet outside of the foundation. This joint may be made by allowing the iron pipe to enter the clay pipe, and then cementing the joint. For a cesspool of this type, a 3″ clay drain pipe is sufficient.

Maintenance of the Radiator. Job No. 10. At times it is necessary to remove the radiator, in order to paint or paper the wall behind it, or to refinish the floor under it. Removal of the radiator should not be attempted when the heating system is turned on. At a time when the fire is low, turn off the valve controlling the admission of steam to the radiator and disconnect this valve from the radiator by unscrewing the hex union nut on the valve. Be sure to turn this nut in the correct direction, as too much tightening may cause it to jam, making it impossible to remove without deforming it. The nut draws the nipple on the radiator side into a brass seat in the valve to form the union and should be unscrewed in a clockwise direction when facing the valve.

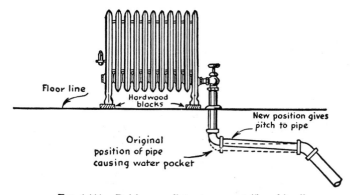

FIG. 4.111.   Raising a radiator to prevent "knocking."

Provision must be made for draining any water that may be left in the radiator by placing a shallow pan under the joint. After the nut is removed, jar the radiator loose from the valve and drain the radiator by tipping it up on edge. Care should be taken not to mark the floor when moving the radiator. If the radiator legs are placed on a heavy rug the radiator may be moved easily from place to place by sliding the rug along the floor. This will also prevent marring the floor.

Pounding or knocking sounds in the pipes of a steam heating system are caused by water being trapped in a section of pipe that has improper pitch. A similar condition may be found in a radiator, if the floor on which the radiator stands is not level. The condition in the radiator may be remedied by setting the legs at one end of the radiator on small wooden blocks to give the pipes sufficient pitch to allow the condensed water in the pipe and fittings to return to the boiler.

The radiator is again connected to the valve by first placing it in the proper position so that the nipple on the radiator will be properly seated in the valve. The union nut is then screwed on to the valve by hand and tightened with a wrench. A large monkey wrench is preferred for use in tightening this nut, as a Stillson wrench will tend to crush the nut and thus cause a leak. Do not force the nut on the threads when starting. Be sure the first thread is caught properly, as injury to the threads may make it necessary to replace the entire valve.

It is a good plan to drain and flush the sediment from each radiator periodically. If the house is to be closed in the winter, each radiator should be disconnected and drained.

A common trouble with radiators in a one-pipe heating system is that some radiators do not heat as quickly as others. The function of the air-vent valve is to remove the air in the radiator in order for the steam to enter the radiator. If the valve is stuck, the air will become trapped in the radiator and the radiator will not heat. A valve that is stuck may be loosened by removing the valve and jarring it vigorously. If there is a question whether or not the air valve is functioning properly, it should be replaced with a new valve. The money invested in an adjustable automatic air vent will be soon saved in the fuel bill. These adjustable valves may be regulated so that the radiators farther away from the furnace will heat at the same time as those close to the furnace. It is false economy to install one or two good valves in a system and then use cheap valves in other parts, as the adjustable valves will be effective only if they are used throughout.

Leaks around the radiator shut-off valve should be taken care of immediately. Considerable damage may be done to the ceiling in the room below if they are allowed to exist. The sputtering of steam around the valve stem may be stopped by tightening the packing nut with an end wrench. If this does not stop the sputtering, new packing should be placed in the packing nut. Special packing may be obtained for this purpose, or it may be packed with wicking as explained in Job No. 2.

Leakage around the union nut is caused by improper fitting of the union. This may be due to dirt in the union fitting, which may be remedied by cleaning the union seat and tightening the union nut with a large wrench.

Leaks of this kind are wasteful because they provide an opening in the system which will prevent the formation of a partial vacuum. Since radiators deliver heat chiefly by convection, it is not usually a good plan to enclose them, as the enclosure or cover will retard the circulation of air.

Radiators recessed in a wall should be provided with sufficient space to allow convection currents of air to pass freely around them. The most efficient radiator is the one that has the most surface. The new type of radiator with the smaller tubes gives off more heat than the old type of radiator that occupies the same space. Some of the heat given off by the radiator is in the form of radiation. This heats the wall behind the radiator and is lost if the wall is an outside one. This loss of heat may be minimized by placing a metal-surfaced reflector behind the radiator.

Maintenance of the Heating Unit. Job No. 11. There is a certain amount of work to be done on the furnace each year in order to keep it operating economically. A few hours' care in the spring, after the heating system is shut off, will save a good deal in fuel and upkeep during the following year. As there are many types and makes of heating units, only the most general maintenance jobs will be covered in this section.

Furnaces should be thoroughly cleaned to remove soot and scale from the interior surface. Starting at the uppermost section with a stiff wire brush with a long handle, brush the sides of the furnace free from scale. Large deposits of soot may be pushed into the ash pit by using a tool shaped like a hoe. Clean out each section above the fire pot, allowing the soot and scale to fall into the ash pit. The smoke pipe should be removed, cleaned, and examined to see whether or not it needs to be replaced. Joints where the smoke pipe enters the chimney and connects to the furnace should be made airtight. The chimney joint can be made airtight by the use of a cement, which is a mixture of 3 parts asbestos powder with 1 part Portland cement.

Firebrick and fire pot linings should be examined and replaced if they are cracked. The furnace grate should be examined and, if badly burned away, should be replaced. Dirt and scale should be scraped from the doors. Loose parts, such as the joint where the door frame is fastened to the furnace, should be tightened, replacing stove bolts where necessary. Doors that are warped may be made to fit by filing the high edges. Using a coarse file, remove just enough material to make the door fit. Repairs may be made in the asbestos insulation of the furnace as shown on page **37.** The drafts in the furnace should be left open so that air is permitted to circulate through the furnace to prevent rusting. The ash pit should be left about one half full, as the dry ashes tend to absorb moisture. The iron surfaces outside of the furnace may be painted, and the surface inside the furnace may be coated with crankcase oil to prevent rusting.

The water in a steam or hot water boiler should not be drawn off in the spring, as there will be less rusting on the interior surfaces of the boiler if it is left full. In a hot water heating system, all parts of the system should be left full of water. The steam boiler may be filled to the height of the safety valve. Never drain the water that is already in the furnace, as the air in this water has been expelled and, therefore, will cause less rusting than fresh water.

In the fall, the sediment that has accumulated at the bottom of the boiler may be drained from the drain cock near the bottom of the furnace. Just enough water should be removed from the boiler to drain this sediment or to show the proper level of water in the gauge.

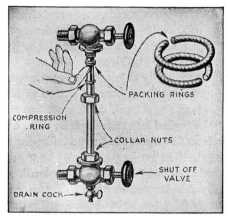

Fig. 4.112.   Replacing water gauge glass on boiler.

A broken water-gauge glass may be replaced by removing the gauge guard rods and loosening the collar nuts at the top and bottom of the glass. A new gauge glass may be obtained in a hardware store. It should be cut slightly longer than the distance between the sockets. The new glass is inserted in the lower socket and then pushed up into the upper socket. Packing is placed around the glass at each socket.

This packing may be made of wicking. It is wound around the glass in the same direction as the nut is turned when tightening. The collar nuts are then tightened just enough to prevent leakage around the collar. A broken gauge glass that cannot be replaced immediately can be removed for a short time if the valves at the top and bottom of the gauge are shut. The water level in the furnace can then be checked by opening the cocks provided near the top and bottom of the gauge. There is sufficient water in the boiler if water runs out of the bottom cock; and the boiler is too full if water runs out of the top cock.

Broken parts of the furnace may be replaced by ordering new ones from the manufacturer, stating the serial number, which appears in a conspicuous place on some part of the furnace. The serial number should always be mentioned and also the pattern number, which usually is cast directly on the part.

It is not advisable to use the furnace as an incinerator for burning rubbish during the summer months as this type of refuse will produce more soot and dirt than normal operation of the furnace.

A thorough check should be made of the heating system in the fall before the fire is built, to make sure that there are no leaks and that the water is at the proper level in the boiler.

INDEX